C000177194

MARK VEEVERS.

PRACTICAL GEMMOLOGY

PRACTICAL GEMMOLOGY

A STUDY OF THE IDENTIFICATION OF GEM-STONES, PEARLS, AND ORNAMENTAL MINERALS

Fifth Edition

BY

ROBERT WEBSTER, F.G.A.

Author of
The Gemmologist's Compendium
Gems: Their Sources, Descriptions and Identification

N.A.G. PRESS LTD.
LONDON

1st Edition	1943
Reprinted	1947
2nd Edition	1952
3rd Edition	1957
Reprinted	1961
4th Edition	1966
Reprinted	1970
5th Edition	1973
6th Edition	1976

I.S.B.N. 7198 0011 0

© Copyright Robert Webster and N.A.G. Press Ltd.,
1943, 1952, 1957, 1966, 1973, 1976

Printed and bound in Great Britain by
Morrison & Gibb Ltd, London and Edinburgh

PREFACE

THE "lessons" comprising this book were first published serially in *The Gemmologist*. Slightly extended, corrected and improved where necessary (facetted and polished, as it were) they are offered as an introduction to the fascinating study of gems and to complement the information and data contained in *The Gemmologist's Compendium*.

Essential methods of gem testing are explained concisely, the apparatus is fully described and, where possible, illustrated. A brief account of the gem species is given in semi-tabular form. *Practical Gemmology* has been kept within manageable size by omitting the more intricate, scientific tests, and long descriptive chapters on gems, all of which are available in existing text-books.

During the past twenty-five years gemmology has advanced considerably and a revised edition has now become imperative. In this revision the needs of the gemmology student have been kept in mind, and to this end a further two "lessons" have been incorporated besides the adjustment of other "lessons." The new "lesson" on chemistry, while perhaps the "heaviest" in the book, is now an essential part of gemmology and cannot be omitted.

The Author wishes to express to Mr. B. W. Anderson and his teaching colleagues thanks for their assistance and advice in this compilation. Special thanks are due to Mr. K. W. Young of the Geology Staff of Northern Polytechnic for kindly making the fine crystal drawings which illustrate the "lesson" on crystallography; and to Dr. E. A. D. White and the Editor of the *G. E. C. Journal* for permission to use the drawings of the Verneuil furnace; the autoclave and the flux-melt crucible which are reproduced in the section on synthetic stones. The Editor of the *Journal of Gemmology* gave permission for the use of the picture of composite stones.

ROBERT WEBSTER.

WIMBLEDON,
    LONDON, S.W.20.

INTRODUCTION

GEMMOLOGY, the science of gems, is comparatively a newcomer to the arts of learning. Despite the fact that it has a commercial aspect, it is a subject of absorbing interest to one and all alike. As the materials used for personal adornment throughout the ages are so varied, so are the true sciences to which the students must turn for assistance in the understanding of gem materials—and this combined knowledge forms the basis for the new science of gemmology.

Since 90 per cent of gem materials are products of the mineral kingdom it is obvious that a definite knowledge is required of the sciences of mineralogy and geology. The chemist plays his part in the study of gems and counterfeits, while the basic methods of gem discrimination, as used today, depend upon the work of the great physicists from Newton onwards. The gem materials of animal origin, as exemplified by pearl, ivory and coral, and of the vegetable kingdom, by amber and jet, bring in the work of the zoologist, the biologist and the botanist.

In any study of gems it is usual, and indeed advantageous, to deal with the subject from the angle of the mineral gemstones, leaving those of animal and vegetable origin to fall into their allotted places as later discussions, a method which will be carried out in this series.

The first of the three cardinal virtues of a gemstone is undoubtedly beauty—through transparency and depth of colour as in the ruby and emerald, through colour only as in the turquoise, through purity and "fire" as in the diamond, and through "play of colour" as in the opal. Finally, there is the beauty brought out by the lapidary in cutting the stone, often latent until he gets to work.

For use as ornaments, a cut stone should be able to resist abrasive influences that tend to destroy its lustre, so that durability is the second of the cardinal virtues. Durability is governed by the hardness of the minerals, and gemstones are in general hard minerals. Paste (glass) is not durable; it is too soft to resist the abrasion of the sand and dust particles in the air and the chemical action of the sulphur in the atmosphere.

Often of far greater influence than either beauty or durability is the third virtue, rarity. A mineral may be fairly common yet really fine pieces suitable for cutting may be quite rare. An example of this is the emerald; a flawless emerald of fine colour is exceedingly rare and may command a higher price than the diamond. The law of supply and demand, often influenced by the caprice of fashion, governs to a certain extent the rarity of gemstones, for there are many stones which undeniably possess the qualifications of beauty and durability but which have little value at the moment owing to the lack of demand.

Gemstones are divided into two classes as precious stones and semi-precious stones, but the division is quite arbitrary. In commercial circles, precious stones are usually understood to be diamond, ruby, sapphire, emerald and pearl with, perhaps, black opal, all stones where the value for fine specimens is high and for which demand is fairly constant. Semi-precious stones, such as peridot, aquamarine, tourmaline, zircon, etc., do not command such a high value and their demand is more prone to the whims of fashion. The term *semi-precious* has little true meaning and is now discouraged.

As gemstones are minerals and are found in rocks, a note on minerals and rocks is given briefly. Minerals, as a rule, have a more or less definite chemical composition, which can be expressed by a formula; and, like other chemical compounds, are homogeneous; while rocks may be defined as aggregates of several minerals, which may vary very much in their relative proportions and which may be, more or less, easily separated, *e.g.* common granite is a rock which is made up of three principal constituent and easily observed minerals: feldspar, mica and quartz; each of these three minerals are definite chemical compounds and may be mixed in almost any proportion to form granite.

Rocks are usually divided into three groups. The *igneous* (fire-formed) rocks being those which have formed from molten rocks which are found in the lower parts of the earth's crust. They may be coarse-grained or fine-grained. A very coarse-grained type, called *pegmatite*, is an important source of gem minerals. Granite and obsidian are examples of igneous rocks, the first being formed by slow cooling and the second by quick cooling of the molten rock. It is in cavities in such rocks that a number of gem minerals are found.

Sedimentary rocks are layered rocks formed by the denudation of pre-existing rocks. Sandstones and limestones are such rocks. Except for turquoise and opal these rocks are the source of few gem minerals. The denudation of rocks by weathering and by the action of rivers can produce a loose "rock." The sand of the sea shore is technically such a rock due to the weathering of sandstones. When the original rock contained heavy minerals, and gem minerals are heavy minerals, pebbles of them tend to be deposited in hollows of river beds of recent or ancient ages. It is in these beds either as present rivers or as the dried-up beds of ancient rivers that the so-called *alluvial* deposits are produced. Such deposits form the gem gravels of Upper Burma, which is called the *byon*, and those of Ceylon called *illam*.

The third type of rock, the *metamorphic* rocks, are pre-existing rocks which have been altered by intrusions of igneous rocks, or by pressures due to earth movements. Marble is produced from limestone by such an action, and when the original limestone contained impurities these may also reform and produce other minerals in the marble. Some Burmese ruby is formed this way. Such rocks are a fruitful source of gem minerals.

Any study of minerals soon shows that many occur naturally in geometrical forms bounded by plane surfaces which are termed crystals, a name derived from the Greek *crystallos*, meaning ice. The Greek philosophers thought that the brilliant crystal of colourless quartz (rock crystal) was water turned to ice which had been compressed in the mountain regions to such an extent that permanent congealment had taken place. A study of these bodies does not appear, at first sight, to be of great importance in the science of gems, but nearly all gems are cut from crystals and the crystalline form is just an outward sign of an inward orderly arrangement of the molecules which build up the structure of any kind of matter.

These molecules, so small that no microscope can be devised that will allow them to be seen, are the smallest particles of a compound that still remains as the compound, viz. a molecule of water is the smallest particle of water that can still remain alone and preserve the character of water. The molecules in a crystal are arranged in accordance with a definite plan which differs with every kind of crystalline type; it is by the physical and optical effects caused by this orderly arrangement that the various gems can be differentiated from each other and from glass. Glass has no regularity in the arrangement of its constituent molecules, hence, it has no definite structure. It must be understood that while a molecule is correctly defined as the smallest part of a compound (or element) that can still have the characters of a compound, in the case of crystals a number of molecules must be linked together in a certain pattern before the unique properties of the crystal are established.

Crystals can weigh as much as several tons, or be so small and so packed together that even the most powerful microscope will not reveal their boundaries. Such material is termed crypto-crystalline, an example of which is cornelian. Material which possesses the definite internal molecular structure of a crystal but which does not show the outward geometrical form is termed massive crystalline material, and rose quartz is a well-known example. Material that possesses no orderly molecular arrangement is termed non-crystalline or amorphous. Glass is of this type and so are the natural and synthetic resins (amber and bakelite) and opal, which is a natural gem.

THE CHEMISTRY OF GEMSTONES

ALL the material things that we know, whether they be solids, liquids or gases, are composed of one or more fundamental substances known as the *elements*. Whereas most materials are *compounds* or mixtures of compounds and can be analysed by suitable means into simpler substances a chemical element cannot be broken down into anything more simple except by extreme physical forces which will be explained later. There are some ninety different elements, embracing solids such as iron or sulphur, liquids such as mercury and bromine, and gases such as oxygen and nitrogen.

The science of chemistry is concerned with the properties and behaviour of these elements and their compounds in their reactions to one another. Chemical reactions always involve a change in the nature of substances involved, and in this way *chemical* properties are conveniently distinguished from *physical* properties, in which there is no permanent change in the nature of the substances concerned. Thus, being attracted by a magnet is a physical property of iron: the fact that it reacts and is dissolved by nitric acid is a chemical property involving drastic changes in both substances.

It is important to understand the difference between a *mixture* of two substances and a *chemical compound* formed between them. In a mixture of, say, iron filings and sulphur each constituent can be present in any proportion, and the two substances can readily be separated, *e.g.* by removing the iron by means of a magnet. But when iron and sulphur are roasted together they combine in definite proportions to make the chemical compound iron sulphide, having none of the properties of either iron or sulphur, and it is no longer possible to separate the iron from the sulphur by physical means.

In gemmology, the physical properties of minerals are naturally more important than the chemical, since we can measure them without altering or harming the stones in any way, whereas chemical tests, however delicate, always involve some destruction of the material. But some understanding of the basic facts of chemistry and of the composition of gemstones is essential for the student if he is to get a true picture of the mineral world.

Even in Roman times, the poet and philosopher Lucretius surmised that all matter could be divided into elementary particles or atoms. Early in the nineteenth century John Dalton postulated that atoms are discrete particles of matter which cannot be subdivided by any chemical process, and that all atoms of any element are similar to each other but differ from the atoms of any other element. Careful measurements of the exact proportions by weight in which various elements combined with one another enabled chemists to arrive at the relative weights of their atoms. These "*atomic weights*" were originally calculated with the lightest atom, that of hydrogen, as unity. Later, it became more convenient to make them relative to oxygen = 16·00, which actually involved very little change.

The whole rather chaotic field of chemical knowledge was made vastly more orderly when the great Russian chemist Mendeléeff discerned a periodic similarity amongst the elements when these were arranged in order of their atomic weights. His tabulation of the known elements in groups according to his "Periodic system" not only brought out the close similarity of certain elements, such as the alkali metals lithium, sodium and potassium; the alkaline earth metals calcium, strontium and barium; the halogen elements chlorine, bromine and iodine, and so on, but showed that there were certain "gaps" in the table waiting to be filled by rarer elements not yet discovered. One of Mendeléeff's triumphs was that he was able to describe with fair accuracy the probable properties of the missing elements, some of which were discovered in his lifetime. Since his day all the gaps have been filled, including a complete unsuspected group of rare gases which were discovered in the atmosphere towards the close of the century, of which argon is the most plentiful. These so-called "noble gases" are chemically inert, and they play an important part in the general theory of atomic structure, as explained in a condensed form below.

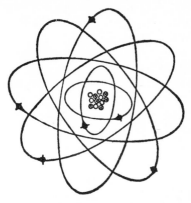

Fig. 1.—Schematic diagram of the structure of the carbon atom. In the core or nucleus the circles with a cross represent protons and the plain circles neutrons. The full black discs with cross bars are the electrons.

It is now known that the atom is itself divisible by physical means, and indeed consists of three smaller particles. These are the *electron*, the *proton* and the *neutron*. The atom consists of a heavy core, the *nucleus*, which contains, except in the hydrogen atom, a number of protons and neutrons. This nucleus is surrounded by a "cloud" of planetary electrons to complete the atom (fig. 1). The proton is the unit positive charge of electricity and has the mass of 1; the neutron is an uncharged particle with a similar mass, and the electron is the unit negative electrical charge and has a mass of only 1/1850 that of the proton. In a full atom the number of electrons equals the number of protons so the atom is electrically neutral. The number of protons in the nucleus gives the "atomic number" of the element. The combined weights of the particles give the atomic weight of the element, but, as will be explained later, there are complications here.

The planetary electrons have a definite special arrangement. They circle the nucleus in "shells," called *energy levels*, which are at different distances from the core. There can be only two electrons in the inner-most shell; eight each in the two next shells; eighteen each in the next

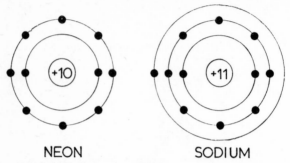

NEON   SODIUM

FIG. 2.—The fully filled outer ring of electrons in the stylized diagram of the neon atom shows it to be a noble gas. The atom of sodium has one electron in the outer ring. Potassium has this ring filled with its eight electrons and the next and now outer ring has one electron. Thus the electronic configuration is similar to that of sodium and both elements have similar chemical characteristics.

two and thirty-two in the next full shell, the outer shell not being complete. When there are just enough electrons to complete a shell the element concerned is chemically inert—they are the so-called "noble gases." Further, those elements with a similar electronic configuration, *i.e.* the same number of electrons in the outer shell, have similar chemical properties (fig. 2).

The planetary electrons are not rigorously attached to the nucleus and they can be removed from its influence, or can even gain one or more electrons. This produces a charged atom which is called an *ion*. A gain of electron/s produces a negatively charged ion, called an *anion*; and a loss of electron/s gives a positively charged ion known as a *cation*. Ions play an important part in forming chemical compounds and crystals.

The hydrogen atom, which has only one proton and one planetary electron, may lose the electron and then produce the particle which is a single proton. Again the removal of the two electrons from the helium atom, whose nucleus contains two protons and two neutrons, produces the particle which is known as the *alpha particle*.

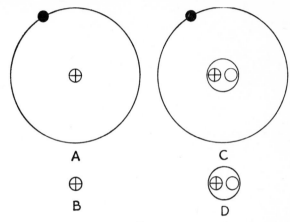

FIG. 3

A. Stylized diagram of the hydrogen atom.
B. Loss of electron of the hydrogen atom leaves an ion. In this case only the proton with unit positive charge.
C. An isotope of hydrogen is the Deuterium which has an extra particle, the neutron, in the nucleus.
D. By loss of the electron Deuterium becomes the particle known as the Deuteron.

Not all the atoms of a given element have the same number of neutrons, and elements of the same kind which have different numbers of neutrons are called *isotopes*. Usually an element consists of a mixture of isotopes and this is the cause of the atomic weight of an element not being a whole number as calculated by chemists in their tables. An example of an isotope which interest gemmologists is that of hydrogen. Normally consisting of one proton and one electron, should the nucleus take in another neutron, "heavy hydrogen," or as it is known—*deuterium* with the symbol D—is produced. The removal of the one electron from deuterium gives the particle called the *deuteron*. The importance of these particles in the study of gemmology is because these are the particles which are used in the atomic coloration of diamond (fig. 3).

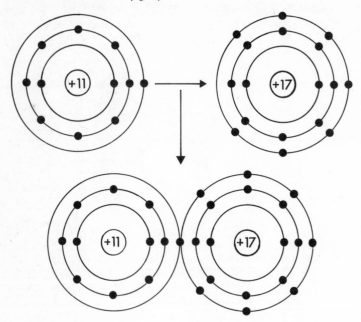

FIG. 4.—The one electron in the outer shell of the sodium atom fills the space of the electron short in the outer shell of the chlorine atom to produce a "noble gas" structure for each atom of sodium chloride (common salt).

A solid substance is produced by atomic bonding of which there are four types, but only two need be mentioned here. They are *ionic bonding*, in which the metallic element or group loses from its outer shell a number of electrons equal to its valency. These join the outer shell of a non-metallic element so as to produce in each element the "octet" structure of a "noble gas" (fig. 4). Oppositely charged ions thus arrange themselves to form a rigid shape to form crystals. No molecules are formed in this case. In *homo-polar bonding* there is a "sharing" of electrons to produce an approach to the "noble gas" structure. This sharing of electrons produces a *molecule*, a name used to describe the smallest discrete particle which can exist (fig. 5). Thus a molecule of aluminium oxide will be the smallest part of the compound which can exist alone, but, as mentioned in the first lesson, it is not the smallest part of a crystal. This being the so-called *unit cell*.

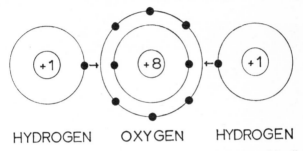

HYDROGEN   OXYGEN   HYDROGEN

FIG. 5.—An oxygen atom with six electrons in its outer ring can "share" the two electrons of two hydrogen atoms to form a molecule of water (H_2O).

A repulsive force sets in at a certain distance when two ions are brought together which resists their closer approach. Considering the ions as spheres in contact the distance between their centres is taken as the sum of the radii of the two ions. This distance differs for different elements; anions are relatively large and cations small, and it is these smaller cations which can replace each other in crystals without unduly straining the crystal lattice. This accounts for the *isomorphous replacement* which is so common in garnets.

Most gemstones are compounds of two or more elements. A chemical reaction to produce a compound can always be related to an equation, but to illustrate these using elemental or compound names would be ungainly, so the chemist has devised a list of symbols, each of which indicates one atom of its element. These symbols are as under.

THE CHEMICAL ELEMENTS

Atomic number	Symbol	Atomic weight	Atomic number	Symbol	Atomic weight
89. Actinium	Ac	227·05	1. Hydrogen	H	1·008
13. Aluminium	Al	26·97	49. Indium	In	114·8
51. Antimony	Sb	121·76	53. Iodine	I	126·93
18. Argon	A	39·94	77. Iridium	Ir	193·1
33. Arsenic	As	74·91	26. Iron	Fe	55·84
56. Barium	Ba	137·36	36. Krypton	Kr	83·7
4. Beryllium	Be	9·02	57. Lanthanum	La	138·9
83. Bismuth	Bi	209·0	82. Lead	Pb	207·2
5. Boron	B	10·82	3. Lithium	Li	6·94
35. Bromine	Br	79·916	71. Lutecium	Lu	175·0
48. Cadmium	Cd	112·41	12. Magnesium	Mg	24·32
55. Caesium	Cs	132·91	25. Manganese	Mn	54·93
20. Calcium	Ca	40·08	80. Mercury	Hg	200·61
6. Carbon	C	12·01	42. Molybdenum	Mo	96·00
58. Cerium	Ce	140·13	60. Neodymium	Nd	144·27
17. Chlorine	Cl	35·457	10. Neon	Ne	20·18
24. Chromium	Cr	52·01	28. Nickel	Ni	58·69
27. Cobalt	Co	58·94	41. Niobium	Nb	92·91
29. Copper	Cu	63·57	7. Nitrogen	N	14·008
66. Dysprosium	Dy	162·46	76. Osmium	Os	190·2
68. Erbium	Er	167·2	8. Oxygen	O	16·00
63. Europium	Eu	152·0	46. Palladium	Pd	106·7
9. Fluorine	F	19·00	15. Phosphorus	P	30·98
64. Gadolinium	Gd	156·9	78. Platinum	Pt	195·23
31. Gallium	Ga	69·72	84. Polonium	Po	210
32. Germanium	Ge	72·60	19. Potassium	K	39·096
79. Gold	Au	197·2	59. Praseodymium	Pr	140·92
72. Hafnium	Hf	178·6	61. Promethium	Pm	147
2. Helium	He	4·003	91. Protactinium	Pa	231·05
67. Holmium	Ho	164·94	88. Radium	Ra	226·05

Atomic number	Symbol	Atomic weight	Atomic number	Symbol	Atomic weight
86. Radon	Rn	222·0	52. Tellurium	Te	127·61
75. Rhenium	Re	186·31	65. Terbium	Tb	159·2
45. Rhodium	Rh	102·91	81. Thallium	Tl	204·39
37. Rubidium	Rb	85·48	90. Thorium	Th	232·12
44. Ruthenium	Ru	101·7	69. Thulium	Tm	169·4
62. Samarium	Sa	150·43	50. Tin	Sn	118·7
21. Scandium	Sc	45·10	22. Titanium	Ti	47·9
34. Selenium	Se	78·96	92. Uranium	U	238·07
14. Silicon	Si	28·06	23. Vanadium	V	50·95
47. Silver	Ag	107·88	74. Wolfram	W	183·92
11. Sodium	Na	22·997	54. Xenon	Xe	131·3
38. Strontium	Sr	87·63	70. Ytterbium	Yb	173·04
16. Sulphur	S	32·064	39. Yttrium	Yt	88·92
73. Tantalum	Ta	180·88	30. Zinc	Zn	65·38
43. Technetium	Tc	99	40. Zirconium	Zr	91·22

Chemical compounds may be quite simple, such as titanium dioxide (TiO_2) which, when in crystal form, is the mineral *rutile*, or immensely complicated as in tourmaline. It is necessary now to give an explanation of the symbol TiO_2 and to do this something must be told about *valency*. Valency has been mentioned earlier in relation to electrons, but now a more chemical approach must be made. The valency of an element is determined by the number of its atoms which will combine with or replace one atom of hydrogen. The valencies of the commoner elements are tabled below. It will be observed that some elements have different valencies in different compounds, *i.e.* in the compound FeO, iron is divalent and Fe_2O_3 it is trivalent.

Monovalent

Bromine	(Br)	Gold	(Au)	Mercury	(Hg)
Chlorine	(Cl)	Hydrogen	(H)	Potassium	(K)
Copper	(Cu)	Iodine	(I)	Silver	(Ag)
Fluorine	(F)	Lithium	(Li)	Sodium	(Na)

Divalent

Barium	(Ba)	Iron	(Fe)	Selenium	(Se)
Beryllium	(Be)	Lead	(Pb)	Strontium	(Sr)
Calcium	(Ca)	Magnesium	(Mg)	Sulphur	(S)
Carbon	(C)	Manganese	(Mn)	Tellurium	(Te)
Chromium	(Cr)	Mercury	(Hg)	Tin	(Sn)
Cobalt	(Co)	Nickel	(Ni)	Zinc	(Zn)
Copper	(Cu)	Oxygen	(O)		

Trivalent

Aluminium	(Al)	Chromium	(Cr)	Manganese	(Mn)
Antimony	(Sb)	Cobalt	(Co)	Nickel	(Ni)
Arsenic	(As)	Gold	(Au)	Nitrogen	(N)
Bismuth	(Bi)	Iron	(Fe)	Phosphorus	(P)
Boron	(B)				

Tetravalent

Carbon	(C)	Silicon	(Si)	Titanium	(Ti)
Lead	(Pb)	Strontium	(Sr)	Zirconium	(Zr)
Manganese	(Mn)				

Pentavalent

Antimony	(Sb)	Bismuth	(Bi)	Phosphorus	(P)
Arsenic	(As)	Nitrogen	(N)	Tantalum	(Ta)

In the above list it will be seen that as titanium is tetravalent and oxygen is divalent it needs two oxygens to satisfy the titanium in order to produce the compound titanium dioxide (TiO_2).

Something needs to be said about the formation of salts when an acid reacts with a base. An *acid* may be defined as a substance which contains hydrogen replaceable either directly or indirectly by a metal; and a *base* is a substance which will react with an acid to form a salt. A *salt* is, therefore, a compound obtained by replacing the hydrogen of an acid by a metal. If all the hydrogen of the acid is replaced the salt is called a *normal salt*; if only a part of the hydrogen is replaced the salt is called an *acid salt*. Some salts can be basic; and some salts are formed by a process of double decomposition. An equation illustrating the formation of a salt—in this case sodium chloride (common salt)—is as follows:

$$HCl \quad + \quad NaOH \quad = \quad NaCl \quad + \quad H_2O$$

| Hydrochloric | Sodium | Sodium | Water |
| acid | hydroxide | chloride | |

Most of the gemstones are either *oxides*, such as aluminium oxide, which when crystallized is the mineral corundum (Al_2O_3) which the gemmologist knows better as sapphire; *sulphides*, formed by the combination of a metal with sulphur (*pyrites* is sulphide of iron); *phosphates*, which are formed by the interaction of a metal or metal groups with phosphoric acid. The most important group of minerals are the *silicates* which can be considered as derived from various silicic acids.

The properties of minerals (of which gemstones are the most attractive varieties) are found to depend more upon the arrangement of the atoms (ions) in the crystal than upon the chemical nature of the compound. In turn the arrangement of ions depends largely upon their relative sizes (or effective radii). In the old days chemists toiled to make some sort of neat chemical formula from chemically complex minerals such as tourmaline. In modern times the X-ray crystallographer has been able to reveal the essentially simple structure of such a mineral and the apparent chemical complexity is seen to be due to the large variety of isomorphous replacements of one ion by another of similar size that can take place in the structure.

No short chapter can give a full exposition of the science of chemistry, but these notes should give all that is needed for a student to study gemmology. It may be of value to conclude this lesson with remarks on a certain type of mineral formulae which sometimes causes confusion in the student's mind. Such a formula is that for topaz

—$Al_2(OH, F)_2SiO_4$. Firstly consider the symbol OH. These two letters indicate the *hydroxyl radical* which acts as a monovalent atom; and secondly the symbols in brackets simply imply that the fluorine and hydroxyl radical can interchange by any amount in the composition. Thus one can get a fluorine-rich or a hydroxyl-rich topaz.

CRYSTALLOGRAPHY

THE study of crystals can rarely be vizualized, by a novice student, as being of value to gem study and the drier parts are in consequence often skipped. It must be said at once that the study of crystals *is of fundamental importance*, for much of the later work could not be understood without the knowledge which elementary crystallography gives.

The study of crystals has not only a value in gem *testing*, but is an essential knowledge for the lapidary who cuts a stone from a crystal, for the different effect of light passing through a crystal in different directions may materially alter the resultant colour and beauty of the stone. Likewise the knowledge of cleavage directions in a crystal often allows it to be easily split in a certain way, so saving much time and labour in cutting, or to avoid having that direction of weakness which would be detrimental in a cut stone. Again a knowledge of crystal symmetry allows a rough crystal to be recognized as belonging to such and such a system, thus allowing the possibility of naming the species by eye inspection alone.

The faces of a crystal are arranged according to certain laws of symmetry which form the natural basis of the classification of crystals into thirty-two groups and seven systems. A discussion of the types of symmetry is not essential for the study of gemstones, but for completeness the elements of symmetry are given. They are *axes of symmetry, planes of symmetry* and *centre of symmetry*.

An axis of symmetry is an axis about which rotation of a crystal will cause it to occupy the same position in space more than once in a complete turn. This may occur twice giving a digonal axis, three times when it is a trigonal axis, four times or tetragonal axis and six times or hexagonal axis (fig. 6). A plane of symmetry is a plane in an

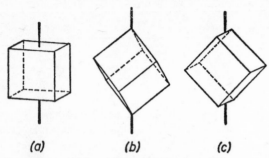

(a)   *(b)*   *(c)*

FIG. 6.—The four-fold, three-fold and two-fold axes of symmetry in a cube.

ideally developed crystal which will divide it in such a way that one side of each plane is the mirror image of the other (fig. 7). A centre of symmetry occurs when like faces and edges occupy corresponding positions on opposite sides of a central point.

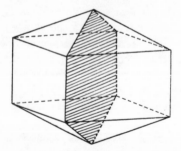

FIG. 7.—A plane of symmetry in a crystal.

To describe the form of a crystal it is necessary to have certain fixed lines of reference from which can be measured the distance and inclination of the various faces, hence, we imagine lines of indefinite length running through the ideal crystal in certain definite directions and intersecting at the centre of it at a point called the *origin* (fig. 8). These imaginary lines, of which three, and in two cases four, are necessary to describe a crystal, are termed *crystal axes* and according to the relative lengths and inclinations of these axes are separated the various crystals into one or other of the seven crystal systems.

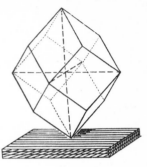

FIG. 8.—Crystal showing the axes. Example is a rhombdo-decahedron of the cubic system.

THE SEVEN CRYSTAL SYSTEMS

In all crystals the combinations of two forms of the same system are common. Through inequalities of growth they rarely conform to the ideal crystal form. In each of the figures of crystals of the different systems an example is given of the combination of two forms.

The CUBIC SYSTEM has three axes all at right angles to one another and all of equal length. There are nine planes of symmetry and three tetragonal, four trigonal and six digonal axes of symmetry (thirteen in all). The ideal forms of the cubic system are the cube, the octahedron, the dodecahedron, (fig. 8) etc.—(also called the REGULAR or ISOMETRIC system) (fig. 9).

Gems which crystallize in the *cubic* system are:

Chromite.	Cobaltite.	Diamond.
Garnet.	Fluorspar.	Pollucite.
Pyrites.	Rhodizite.	Spinel.
Zinc-blende.	Sodalite.	Lazurite.

The TETRAGONAL SYSTEM has three axes, all of which are at right angles to one another, two of which are equal and one unequal in length. The unequal axis is vertical and is known as the principal

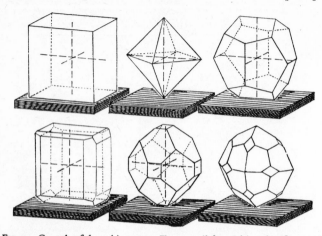

FIG. 9.—Crystals of the cubic system. Top row (*left to right*): cube (fluorspar), octahedron (diamond), pyritohedron (iron pyrites). Bottom row (*left to right*): combination of cube and the pyritohedron (iron pyrites), combination of the cube and rhombdodecahedron (garnet), combination of the icositetrahedron and rhombdodecahedron (garnet).

crystal axis; the equal axes are called the lateral axes. The ideal forms are a prism standing on a square base or two four-sided pyramids on square bases joined base to base. There are five planes of symmetry and one tetragonal and four digonal axes of symmetry (also called the DIMETRIC system) (fig. 10).

Gems which crystallize in the tetragonal system are:

Anatase.	Apophyllite.	Cassiterite.
Idocrase.	Rutile.	Scapolite.
Scheelite.	Zircon.	

The ORTHORHOMBIC SYSTEM has three axes of unequal length which are at right angles to one another. The main axis is placed vertically and the lateral axes pass through the sides; they are termed the *macro axis* for the longer of the two and the *brachy axis* for the shorter. There are three planes of symmetry and three axes of symmetry. The

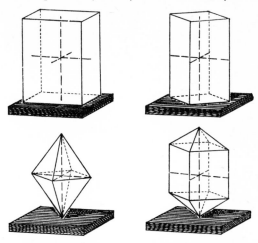

FIG. 10.—Crystals of the tetragonal system. Top left: 2nd order prism and basal pinacoid. Top right: 1st order prism and basal pinacoid. Bottom left: 1st order pyramid. Bottom right: 1st order prism and pyramid in combination (zircon).

ideal forms are a prism on an oblong base (*i.e.* shaped like a matchbox) or the pyramidal form of four-sided pyramids with oblong bases placed base to base (also called the TRIMETRIC system) (fig. 11).

Gems which crystallize in the orthorhombic system are:

Andalusite.	Aragonite.	Beryllonite.
Bronzite.	Chrysoberyl.	Danburite.
Dumortierite.	Enstatite.	Fibrolite.
Hambergite.	Hypersthene.	Iolite.
Kornerupine.	Marcasite.	Peridot.
Prehnite.	Staurolite.	Thomsonite.
Topaz.	Variscite.	Zoisite.
	Sinhalite.	

The MONOCLINIC SYSTEM has three axes, all of unequal length, two of which intersect each other at an oblique angle, while the third is perpendicular to them. One axis is placed vertically and of the other two *lateral axes*, the one at right angles to the vertical axis is called the

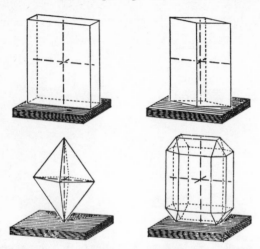

FIG. 11.—Crystals of the orthorhombic system. Top left: the macro, brachy and basal pinacoids. Top right: prism and basal pinacoid. Bottom left: pyramids. Bottom right: combination of forms (peridot).

ortho axis and the axis which is inclined, the *clino axis*. There is one plane of symmetry and one digonal axis of symmetry. The form may be better expressed by assuming a prism on an oblong base which has been pushed on one side, making it lean over slightly in one direction only (fig. 12).

Gems which crystallize in the monoclinic system are:

Azurite.	Datolite.	Diopside.
Epidote.	Euclase.	Gypsum.
Jadeite.	Lazulite.	Malachite.
Meerschaum.	Nephrite.	Orthoclase feldspar.
Serpentine.	Sphene.	Spodumene.
Brazilianite.	Talc.	

The TRICLINIC SYSTEM has three axes all inclined to one another and of unequal length. One axis is placed vertically and the two lateral

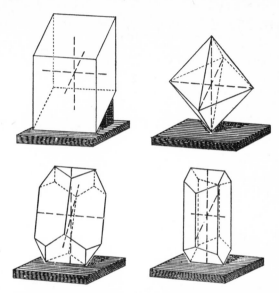

FIG. 12.—Crystals of the monoclinic system. Top left: ortho, clino and basal pinacoids. Top right: hemi-pyramids. Bottom left: combination of prism, orthopinacoid, hemi-pyramid and the basal pinacoid (sphene). Bottom right: combination of prism, basal pinacoid, clinopinacoid and negative hemi-orthodome (orthoclase).

axes are called the *macro* and *brachy* as in the rhombic system. The form may be recalled by the same form as in the monoclinic system with the difference the push should be given to the edge so that the prism leans over both backwards and sideways (fig. 13). This system has no symmetry planes or axes.

Gems which crystallize in the triclinic system are:

Amblygonite.	Rhodonite.	Kyanite.
Axinite.	Labradorite.	Microcline.
Turquoise.	Oligoclase feldspar.	

The HEXAGONAL SYSTEM has four axes. A vertical or principal axis which is longer or shorter than the other three; the lateral axes, which are all of equal length and intersect at 60° with each other. The principal axis is at right angles to the plane containing the lateral axes.

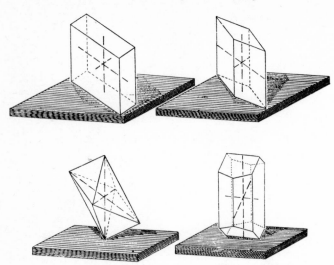

FIG. 13.—Crystals of the triclinic system. Top left: macro, brachy and basal pinacoids. Top right: basal pinacoid and hemi-prisms. Bottom left: quarter pyramids. Bottom right: hemi-prisms, brachy pinacoid, basal pinacoid and the hemi-macrodome (albite feldspar).

The ideal form is a prism on a six-sided base or the bi-pyramidal form of two six-sided pyramids on a common six-sided base. There are seven planes of symmetry and seven axes of symmetry (one hexagonal and six digonal) (fig. 14).

The gems which crystallize in the hexagonal system are:

Apatite.   Beryl.

The TRIGONAL (or RHOMBOHEDRAL) SYSTEM can be referred to the four crystal axes as in the hexagonal system, but this system has lower

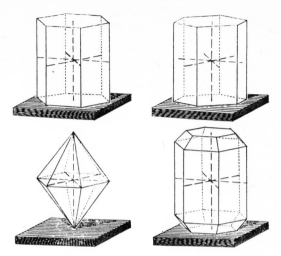

FIG. 14.—Crystals of the hexagonal system. Top left: 1st order prism and basal pinacoid (emerald). Top right: 2nd order prism and basal pinacoid (emerald). Bottom left: 1st order pyramid. Bottom right: 1st order prism, 1st order pyramid and basal pinacoid (beryl).

symmetry. There being only three planes of symmetry and one trigonal and three digonal axes of symmetry (fig. 15).

Gems which crystallize in the trigonal system are:

Calcite.	Corundum.	Dioptase.
Quartz.	Hæmatite.	Phenakite.
Benitoite.	Smithsonite.	Tourmaline.
	Willemite.	

A *form* of a crystal consists of all the faces which are similarly related to the crystal axes, and these may be *pyramid forms* which usually consist of groups of triangular faces each of which cuts three crystal axes, or would do so if both faces and axes were produced. An example of this is the octahedron. *Prism faces* have three or more similar faces meeting in parallel edges. These may be *first order* where each face cuts two lateral axes and is parallel to the vertical axis, or the *second order* where each face cuts only one lateral axis and is parallel to the other two. This of course does not hold good for the hexagonal system which has four axes and thus complicates this simple explanation. The *pinacoid forms* are pairs of similar faces cutting one axis and

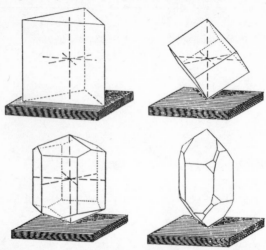

FIG. 15.—Crystals of the trigonal system. Top left: trigonal prism and basal pinacoid. Top right: the rhombohedron (calcite). Bottom left: 1st order hexagonal prism and rhombohedron (calcite). Bottom right: hexagonal 1st order prism, positive and negative rhombohedra, trigonal pyramid and trigonal trapezohedron (quartz).

parallel to the other two (or three in the hexagonal and trigonal systems. The *basal* pinacoid is that which is parallel to the plane containing the lateral axes. *Dome forms* is the name given to a form whose faces intersect the vertical axis and one other and is parallel to the third axis.

Some other terms used in the study of crystals may be briefly mentioned, such as the *closed form* and the *open form*. The first is the form that by itself can enclose space. Thus, the six square faces of the cube can themselves form a solid figure, but the hexagonal prism faces cannot by themselves form a solid figure as they need the top and bottom to be completed by pinacoids which is another form entirely. The hexagonal prism is therefore an open form. Some crystals possess only half the full number of faces required by the fullest symmetry of the system to which they belong, *e.g.* the tetrahedron has only half the number of faces of the octahedron. Such crystals are called *hemihedral* forms. Certain crystals present different forms at opposite ends of an axis of symmetry, which is generally the vertical axis, and thus show different terminations at either end. This is known as *hemimorphism* and such hemimorphic crystals often show electrical effects, *e.g.* tourmaline.

TWIN CRYSTALS: The crystals that have been discussed so far are single individuals; there are, however, occurrences of crystals which consist of two or more individuals and are known as *compound* or *twin crystals*. A *contact twin* is one in which the individuals are in contact along a common plane, the two parts of such a crystal are so related that if one-half is rotated through 180° about an axis, known as the *twinning axis*, it would bring them both into parallel position—*i.e.* reform the two halves so as to make the shape of a single individual crystal. This form is typical of spinel and shows re-entrant angles, a common property of nearly all twin crystals. *Interpenetrant twins* are those in which the two individuals have so intergrown that they penetrate one another. This form may produce such cross-like twins as those of staurolite, which are better known in jewellery as *cross-stones*, or *fairy-stones*. *Repeated, cyclic or polysynthetic twins* are composed of a number of microscopically small contact twins producing a number of very thin plates, each of which is arranged in opposite order to its fellow. This is sometimes called *laminar* or *lamellar twinning* and gives rise to such colour effects as are seen in labradorite (fig. 16). So-called *secondary twinning* or *parting* is presumed to be produced in a crystal subsequent to its original formation, and pressure is generally considered to be the cause. The effect is commonly seen in ruby which is often composed of very thin plates parallel to definite crystallographic directions.

Habit is the general aspect of crystals and minerals. It embraces not only the faces most commonly displayed but the markings and even the flattening or elongation of such faces. Habit often varies in crystals of the same species but from different localities, or by different varieties of the same species. The usual habit of diamond is octahedral; that of ruby rhombohedral, and that of sapphire bi-pyramidal, but some sapphire forms short tabular hexagonal prisms. The usual habit

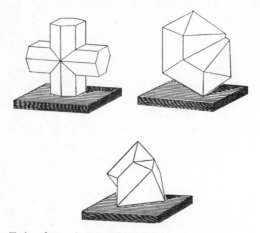

FIG. 16.—Twinned crystals. Top left: staurolite twin, so-called "cross-stone" (orthorhombic). Top right: geniculate (knee-shaped) twin crystal of zircon (tetragonal). Bottom: spinel twin (cubic).

of tourmaline is prismatic and that of garnet is dodecahedral. The slender needle-like crystals seen as inclusions in rock crystal, such as the rutile fibres in Venus hair stone, are termed acicular crystals, and the branch-like inclusions such as are seen in moss agate are known as dendritic inclusions. Radiating crystals forming spherical or hemi-spherical masses produce the so-called *globular* habit or *botryoidal* habit which is common in some chalcedony and prehnite. *Granular* material consists of an aggregate of large or small grains and is exemplified by quartzite and marble. *Stalagmitic* material is formed by deposition of minerals from water solution and may form stalactites which are pendant cylinders from the roof of caves, or stalagmites which are the converse of stalactites in that they grow upwards from the floor of the cave below the stalactite. If they join they form a column. The deposit may also spread along the floor of the cave to produce a banded marble or rhodochrosite. A mineral whose external form is not the one usually associated by its particular species is a *pseudomorph*. The original material here, which may have been inorganic or organic, has been replaced particle by particle, with another mineral, but it usually keeps the form of the original substance.

PHYSICAL PROPERTIES

THE first of the physical properties of gem materials is the phenomenon known as *cohesion*. Cohesion is the force of attraction which holds together the molecules of a substance and the stronger this force of attraction the more difficult it is to break the body. When a body is broken it is said to be *fractured*, and the surface of the fracture may be found to take one of several types. *Conchoidal* fracture shows a number of more or less concentric ridges which resemble the lines on seashells; this type of fracture is typical of rock crystal and glass. Other types of fracture are known as *smooth*, when the surface, without being absolutely plane, presents no marked irregularities; *splintery*, when the surface is covered with partially separated splinters in irregular fibres —an example is fibrous haematite; *hackly*, when the surface is covered with ragged points and depressions. Of far greater importance than fracture is *cleavage*, which is a direction of weakness along which, or parallel to which, if force be applied, a body will easily split. Cleavage is only possible in a crystal or in crystalline material and is due to the molecules making up the crystal being in regular layers (the orderly arrangement) and the force of attraction may be weaker between these layers than across them, hence, will break more readily along such directions; such a direction is known as the *cleavage plane* and is always parallel to a possible crystal face. Cleavage is of assistance in gem cutting or can be a disadvantage in that if an easily cleavable stone is dropped there is a great liability for it to break in two, or, if this major misfortune does not occur, to set up internal flaws which tend to destroy the transparency and with further rough handling increase in size.

Gems which have easy cleavage are:

Diamond.	Euclase.	Fluorspar.
Feldspar.	Sphene.	Spodumene.
Topaz.	Fibrolite.	Calcite.
	Hambergite.	

HARDNESS

There is one other property of all substances which depends upon molecular cohesion, and that is the property termed *hardness*. Hardness may be defined as the power a substance possesses to resist abrasion (scratching) when a pointed fragment of another substance is drawn across it without sufficient pressure to develop cleavage. Experiment shows that a harder stone will scratch a softer object, and, based on this fact, the mineralogist Mohs devised a scale of reference which has been named after him. This is not a scale comparable with the 10 decimetres in a metre, but simply implies that topaz is softer than corundum, and fluorspar is harder than calcite. The intervals between numbers are *not* equal, in fact the difference in hardness between diamond (10) and corundum (9) is definitely greater than between corundum (9) and the softest—talc (1).

MOHS'S SCALE

1. Talc.	6. Orthoclase.
2. Gypsum.	7. Quartz.
3. Calcite.	8. Topaz.
4. Fluorspar.	9. Corundum.
5. Apatite.	10. Diamond.

(*Breithaupt proposed to interpolate Mica as 2·5 and Scapolite as 5·5, but they have not been generally adopted.*)

The softer numbers of the scale, Talc and Gypsum, may be scratched by a finger nail, and those up to 6 by a steel knife point, while Quartz and the higher numbers are all harder than steel. Pointed fragments of the minerals in Mohs's scale numbers 6 to 10

are mounted in wooden or metal stems for use in gem testing.
Working up from the softest to the harder points, the stone under
test has applied to it the various *pencils*, a short line being scratched
on an inconspicuous place (generally near the girdle) and the hardness of the stone will be between the two numbers which will not
leave a scratch mark and the one that does. A better method of
testing for hardness is to use polished plates of minerals of known
hardness and drawing the edge of the stone to be tested across them.
A test that was often resorted to in the early days of this century, it
is now rarely used, more modern and safer scientific methods having
adequately replaced the hardness test.

A short list showing the hardness of the most important gems is
given under:

10. Diamond;
9. Corundum (Ruby and Sapphire);
8½. Chrysoberyl (Alexandrite and Cymophane);
8. Topaz and Spinel;
7½. Beryl (Emerald, Aquamarine, Morganite, and Golden Beryl)
      and Zircon;
7¼. Garnet;
7. Quartz (Amethyst, Citrine, and Rock crystal), Tourmaline
      and Jade (Jadeite);
6½. Spodumene (Kunzite and Hiddenite), Garnet (Demantoid),
      Jade (Nephrite), Rutile;
6. Opal, Moonstone, Strontium titanate and Turquoise;
5½. Sphene;
5. Bowenite serpentine, Lapis lazuli.

Glass imitation gems have a hardness less than 6 on the scale, and in
general the more lustre and "fire" these stones have the softer they are,
for in their manufacture the addition is made to the glass of small
quantities of the oxides of lead and thallium which considerably
softens it. Although on the scale diamond is marked as 10 and
corundum (ruby and sapphire) as 9, it is found that stones from

different localities may vary slightly in hardness. Diamond found in New South Wales (Australia) and Borneo are found to be harder or, at least, harder to cut than the stones from South America which are harder than those from South Africa. Ceylonese sapphires are known to be harder than the sapphires from Kashmir and all sapphires are understood to be somewhat harder than the ruby.

Hardness may vary with direction; in particular is this noticeable in the case of the gem mineral kyanite which shows a hardness of 5 along the length of the crystal and 7 in directions at right angles to the length. Diamond also shows a variation of hardness with direction but the variation is slight.

SPECIFIC GRAVITY

WHICH weighs more, a pound of lead or a pound of feathers? It is one of the "older" catches, which, absurd as it apparently is, concerns a vital point; relation of weight to volume. For the space taken up by the pound of lead is far smaller than the space taken up by the pound of feathers, even if they were compressed to their smallest bulk. Likewise, the comparatively heavy metal, iron, may be said to weigh more than the light metal aluminium, but if two pounds (by weight) of aluminium and one pound (by weight) of iron are taken, it is obvious that the aluminium would be twice as heavy as the iron. Should, however, equal quantities, by size (such as cubes of 1 in. edge), of these metals be taken, it would then be found that the iron cube would weigh approximately three times as much as the cube of aluminium. Thus, it may be said that the *density* of iron is about three times that of aluminium.

A point to remember which is of practical interest is that stones of different species but of the same size will weigh different amounts; hence, if a diamond of a given size is required to be replaced by, say, a strontium titanate, then the difference in weight can be ascertained by using the formula under:

$$\frac{\text{Density of stone required} \times \text{Weight of diamond}}{\text{Density of diamond}}$$

To be of practical value it is necessary to compare the weight of a volume of each substance with the weight of an equal volume of a substance used as a standard. The standard used is pure water at its maximum density, *i.e.* at 4° C. The value given by this ratio is known as the *specific gravity* (the term generally used for solids) or *relative density* (generally used for liquids). The specific gravity (often termed *density* for shortness) is a physical property of all materials, and as a rule is constant between fairly narrow limits for pure substances. Gemstones are mostly pure substances and their specific gravities are, with few exceptions, remarkably constant, hence the property may be used as a means for their distinction, one from another.

At first sight it would appear to be an insurmountable difficulty to obtain the volume of an irregular gemstone so as to compare it with an equal volume of water. It is, however, unnecessary to ascertain the volume of the solid (gemstone), by means of calculation, for if the stone is placed in an Eureka can, a metal vessel with an overflow pipe and filled with water, the displaced water passes through the pipe and can be collected and measured. Thus, if the displaced water is measured in cubic centimetres and the stone weighed in grammes, all the necessary figures for computing the density are at once available (*1 cubic centimetre of water weighs 1 gramme*). Easy as this method appears, it does not lend itself to the accuracy required for small bodies, such as gemstones.

Of far greater accuracy is the variously termed *direct weighing method* or *hydrostatic weighing method*, which depends upon the principle, discovered by the Greek philosopher Archimedes, that a body immersed in a liquid is buoyed up by a force equal to the weight of the liquid it displaces. Therefore, if an object is first weighed in air, and then, when suspended by a thread, in water, it weighs less the second time by an amount equal to the weight of water equal in volume to itself, this weight, divided into the weight of the object, gives the specific gravity.

This method is one of the most important used in gemmological science. It requires the use of a delicate balance. There are special balances marketed for the purpose of specific gravity determination, but they do not appear to be widely used. A good chemical or assay balance or diamond scales answers admirably, as it would have the necessary qualification of being capable of weighing to a milligram

(0·005 carat). One of the most convenient methods of using a plain
chemical balance for specific gravity work is first to prepare a wooden
or metal stool, which will stride the left-hand pan in such a manner
that it does not in any way hinder the swing of the balance. On this
stool is placed a beaker of water, again ensuring that it clears the pan
arms of the balance. From the hook at the end of the beam, from

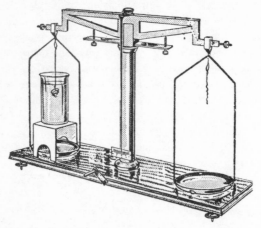

FIG. 17.—The balance set up for hydrostatic weighing.

which is suspended the pan arms, there is placed a loop of fine wire
which carries at its lower end a cage, formed of stouter wire, to take
the stone. It may be formed, cone shaped, around the sharpened end
of a pencil. The cage dips into the water in the beaker so that it is
completely covered during a full swing of the balance. On the similar
hook over the right-hand pan there is placed a piece of wire exactly
counterpoising the wire and cage on the left-hand side when dipping
into the water (fig. 17). The stone under test may now be weighed
in air by placing it in the left-hand pan and adding weights to the
right-hand pan.

In practice it is usual to use the metric carat weights, or the gramme
weights of the metric system. A set of these weights normally contains

the following values: 100, 50, 20, 20, 10, 5, 2, 2, 1, 0·5, 0·2, 0·2, 0·1, 0·05, 0·02, 0·02, 0·01, 0·005, 0·002, 0·002 and 0·001 (carat weights rarely below 0·005), a range from which any combination of weights may be obtained. In many modern balances the smaller weights are dispensed with and a small looped weight, called a *rider*, is slid along the graduated arm of the balance to obtain the readings under one carat.

To commence weighing it is better to begin by placing a weight in the right-hand pan which is in excess of the object to be weighed. Then, working down through the weights of lower values one at a time, ensuring that the balance pans are lowered every time a weight is changed. The worker removes the weights which are too heavy, returning them to the box, and leaving in the pan the weights which are too light. By this method all the weights are passed through in turn until a correct balance is obtained. *The method, if it can be called a method, of dodging about with the weights, sometimes one of higher value, sometimes one of lower, until some sort of balance is obtained is to be deprecated. It gives neither brilliant results nor speed of working.* The weights in the pan are now removed and added together, giving the weight in air of the stone (X in formula).

The stone is now removed from the left-hand pan and placed in the wire cage which is suspended in the water. It is necessary to ensure that there are no air bubbles adhering to the stone. If some are present they may conveniently be removed with the aid of a small camel-hair paint brush. The stone is now weighed in a similar manner as has been explained before, and the result, which will be of lower value, noted. This is the weight of the stone when immersed in water (Y in formula).

The formula for the determination of specific gravity is: $\dfrac{X}{X - Y}$

where X is the weight of the stone in air, Y the weight of the stone when immersed in water. The apparent loss of weight $(X - Y)$ if divided into the weight in air gives the specific gravity.

Example, a red stone weighs 2·063 (carats or grammes) in air, and 1,565 (carats or grammes) when immersed in water, therefore:

Weight of the stone in air   ...   .   2·063
Weight of the stone in water   ...   ... 1·565

                                           —— 4·14 = S.G.

Apparent loss of weight   ...   . 0·498/2·063

                                             1·992

                                             710
                                             498

                                            2120

giving a specific gravity of 4·14, which, on looking-up in a table-book of constants, will be found to be that of almandine garnet.

The density of large specimens which cannot be weighed by an ordinary gem balance may be determined by using a suitably suspended spring balance. The specimen being first weighed in air and then while suspended in water.

However, to conform to the definition of specific gravity, it appears necessary to know whether the water was at a temperature of 4° C., and if it was not, how it affects the final determination of S.G. (*S.G. is the abbreviation for specific gravity.*) To correct the work for temperature of the water it is necessary to ascertain the temperature of the water at the time of the experiment and multiply the answer by the density of the water at the temperature found (*densities of water at different temperatures are published as tables in technical books*). With the example given above it will be supposed that the temperature of the water was 14·7° C. (*density of water at 14.7° C. =* 0·99917) so that 4·14 multiplied by 0·99917 will give 4·13, which gives the density of the stone correct to 4° C. In general gem testing this refinement of temperature correction is unnecessary, nor is there any value in carrying on the division sum to more than two places of decimals, for the drag on the wire, due to the surface tension of the water, precludes real accuracy for more than the second place except for large specimens. To avoid this surface tension a liquid such as benzene, toluene or ethylene dibromide may be used in place of water. Should these liquids be used, it is essential that the correction for temperature is made, for the density of these liquid hydrocarbons is considerably different from that of water and, moreover, varies greatly for changes of temperature.

The methods of density determination just discussed suffer from the disadvantage that the weighing and subsequent calculation take some considerable time. Methods which can be most useful, speedy, and capable of extreme accuracy can be carried out by the use of *heavy liquids*. A stone will float in any liquid which has a higher density than itself, sinks in one of lower density, and in a liquid of the same density it neither floats nor sinks but remains motionless wherever it is placed (termed *freely suspended*), therefore, if a stone is found to remain freely suspended in a liquid, it is only necessary to find, by some means, the density of the liquid to know that of the stone.

The ideal conditions required for a *heavy liquid* are a high density and the capability of intimately mixing with another liquid of lower density for the production of a mixture having any density between the limits of the two fluids. There are many liquids which have the necessary conditions in a varying degree and which have been adopted at various times for gem-testing purposes. Modern practice has selected three as being the most useful. These three liquids are printed in small capitals below:

1. BROMOFORM, a colourless liquid ($CHBr_3$) which has a specific gravity of about 2·86. The density can be lowered by dilution with benzene or toluol (density = 0·88), but monobromonaphthalene (density = 1·49) may be a more convenient liquid to use. Bromoform is useful for stones of low density, such as beryl and quartz.

2. METHYLENE IODIDE (CH_2I_2). Density $= 3\cdot32$. May be diluted with benzene or toluol or bromoform.
3. CLERICI'S SOLUTION (thallium malonate and formate in water). Density $= 4\cdot15$ at room temperature. May be diluted with water. (Is poisonous and stains the skin.)

The density of a liquid, in which a stone under test is found to be freely suspended, may be ascertained by several methods. Of these

FIG. 18.—The pyc-nometer or "specific gravity bottle."

methods, the one necessitating the employment of a *specific gravity bottle* or *pycnometer*, will be discussed first. This method is one of considerable accuracy but its use is mostly confined to work of an exceptional nature for the necessary weighings are time-consuming. The *specific gravity bottle* (fig. 18) is a small glass flask fitted with a ground glass stopper, which is pierced lengthwise by a capillary opening. The flask is generally engraved on the outside with the weight of water it will contain at room temperature ($15°$ C.), so that if the flask is first weighed when empty and again when filled with the liquid whose density is to be determined, the difference between the two weights will give the weight of the liquid. The weight of an equal volume of water is known by the value engraved on the flask (*if not so marked, this can be found by weighing the flask when filled with water and subtracting from this weight the weight of the empty flask*). Then by dividing the weight of the water into the weight of the liquid is ascertained the density of that liquid.

Example.

Weight of water in bottle   50 grammes.
Weight of bottle and liquid   202 grammes.
Weight of bottle ...   ...   35 grammes.
Weight of liquid ...   ...   167 grammes.

Hence, density $= \dfrac{167}{50} = 3\cdot34$ *(correction for temperature as for direct*

weighing method).

Therefore a transparent green stone which remained freely suspended in this liquid would have a specific gravity of 3·34, hence would be a peridot. The specific gravity bottle may also be used for determining the density of small gems, the method being as follows: The stone is weighed (A). The bottle is filled with water and weighed (B). The stone is placed in the bottle of water, the surplus water overflowing over the top and through the hole in the stopper, and the whole weighed (C). The specific gravity is calculated by the formula:

$$\frac{A}{A + B - C}$$

The *Westphal balance* is constructed expressly for the determination of the density of liquids and its essential design is that of a modified Roman balance, or butcher's steelyard (fig. 19). At the end of the graduated arm is suspended a sinker which dips into the liquid whose density is required to be known. This sinker, which contains a small thermometer, is so weighted that when it is immersed in water the balance is accurately counterpoised. So that when the sinker is placed in a liquid denser than water it is buoyed up and it is necessary to place weights on the graduated arm to bring the balance again to the counterpoise position. The weights employed are arbitrary, but are all multiples of some standard weight and the density of the liquid can be read directly from the position of the various weights on the beam.

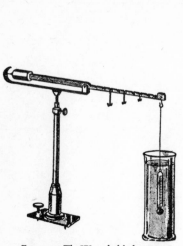 

FIG. 19.—The Westphal balance.

FIG. 20.—A modification of the Westphal balance.

The Westphal balance may be modified to allow it to be used for the direct weighing method. This is carried out by the substitution of the sinker by a pan and clip (fig. 20), and the method of use is as follows: The clip is immersed in water and weights added to the beam until it is counterpoised (A). These weights are then removed, the stone placed in the pan, and weights again added to obtain a counterpoise (B), the clip still remaining in the water. The operation is repeated with the stone enclosed in the clip and immersed in the water (C). Specific gravity is found by the formula:

$$\frac{A - B}{C - B}$$

A method for ascertaining the density of a liquid, while not so accurate as those mentioned previously, is by the use of a suitably graduated hydrometer. A hydrometer of the fixed graduated type is generally made of glass with the base weighted with shot or mercury, and has a narrow stem marked with the density values (fig. 21).

When the instrument is immersed in the liquid under test it floats at a definite level, and if the value shown on the graduated stem at the level of the liquid is read, this reading will give the density of the liquid. Fixed hydrometers are usually constructed to cover only a small range of densities, as a wide range would necessitate an inordinately long stem. A number of these instruments, of different ranges, are necessary if a very full range of density is required to be covered. As the instruments are calibrated at a certain temperature (usually marked on the stem) correction may be required and in using hydrometers, easy and quick as their use may be, care must be taken that they float clear of the sides of the vessel containing the liquid. Likewise, care is necessary to ensure that the reading is taken at the level of the liquid, and not at the top of the curve of the liquid where it meets the stem (*the meniscus*).

FIG. 21.—The hydrometer.

To distinguish between gemstones it is rarely necessary to use such accurate methods and, with *heavy liquids*, comparative methods are considerably more useful. If a series of glass tubes, fitted with corks or ground glass stoppers, are obtained and arranged in a wooden box (certain heavy liquids darken on exposure to light), they may be half-filled with heavy liquids that are suitably diluted so as to give a range of densities. It is unnecessary to be accurate with these densities; for example, if a liquid is made up which will float a quartz (S.G. = 2·65), and in which a beryl (S.G. = 2·7) will sink, the density of the liquid must lie somewhere between 2·65 and 2·7. If a series of tubes are made up to a range of densities, using small gemstones of known species as indicators, or the density "cubes" made by

Rayner, it is possible to ascertain, within limits defined by the nearness of the values of the tubes, the approximate S.G. of a suspected stone by placing them in different tubes, one after another, and noting whether the stone sinks or floats. The range and value a series of tubes are made up to is dictated by the worker's own needs, but for the sake of example, a suggested series is given, as follows:

1. Bromoform diluted with toluene to approximate density of 2·5 (*indicators; gypsum* = 2·3 *and moonstone* = 2·57).
2. Bromoform diluted with toluene to approximate density of 2·7 (*indicators; quartz* = 2·65 *and calcite* = 2·71).
3. Pure bromoform, density = 2·90 (*bromoform is fairly stable so that no indicators are necessary*).
4. Methylene iodide diluted with bromoform to density of 3·1 (*indicator; tourmaline which remains freely suspended*).
5. Pure methylene iodide. Density = 3·32 (*no indicator necessary*).
6. Clerici's solution diluted with water to density of 3·52 (*indicator; small diamond which remains freely suspended*).
7. Clerici's solution diluted with water to approximate density of 3·7 (*indicators; spinel* = 3·60 *and chrysoberyl* = 3·73).
8. Clerici's solution diluted with water to density of 4·0 (*indicator; synthetic ruby freely suspended*).

If the liquids are unused for some time it will be found that the denser indicator will have floated to the top, due to the evaporation of the toluene (or benzene). This evaporation increases the density of the liquid which has to be re-diluted by the addition of a small quantity of toluene. Care is necessary when testing stones, to ensure that they are wiped when they are removed from a tube of liquid and before being placed in another tube, either of the same type of liquid or in a tube containing a liquid of another composition. It is unwise to immerse in liquids such porous stones as turquoise, opals and pearls, or, if it is necessary to use heavy liquids for such gems, they should be quickly removed, rinsed in clean benzene and carefully dried.

Ten level teaspoonfuls of common salt dissolved in a tumbler of water produces a solution having a density between the S.G. of amber (1·08) and the S.G. of the common amber substitute, bakelite (1·26), and other plastic imitations, hence, this solution is a useful addition to the *heavy liquids* for the detection of amber. Amber floats on the salt solution while the imitations sink. It should be noted, however, that this solution will not separate the natural copal resins nor the synthetic resin "polystyrene," which have the same density as true amber.

If a tall glass measure is half-filled with a heavy liquid, and on top of this is gently poured a less dense liquid, but one that is miscible with the first liquid, and left to stand for some time (gentle shaking will assist the process), a column of liquid is formed, by diffusion of the two liquids one with another, which progressively increases in density from top to bottom. This is known as a *diffusion column*. Then supposing three stones of different densities to be gently dropped into the liquid, they would be found to take up stations at different levels, levels where the density of the liquid matches that of the stones It is then quite obvious that if a suspected stone is found to float at a point between the levels taken up by two other stones of known specific gravity, the S.G. of the suspected stone must be somewhere between the densities of the stones acting as indicators. While the diffusion column is useful in detecting small differences of specific gravity, it does not compare in usefulness with the tubes of liquids made up to different densities, either for ease of preparation or for convenience of storing.

Below is appended a short list of the average specific gravities of the most important gemstones. The species name is printed first followed by the variety names, where these are important, *e.g.* ruby and sapphire are merely colour varieties of the species, corundum.

SPECIFIC GRAVITIES

| Amber | 1·08 | Feldspar (moonstone) | 2·57 |
| Opal | 2·1 | Serpentine (bowenite) | 2·58 |

Quartz (rock-crystal, amethyst, citrine)	2·65	Topaz	3·53—3·56
Pearl	2·7	Spinel	3·60
		Garnet (hessonite)	3·65
Beryl (emerald, aquamarine, morganite)	2·71	Chrysoberyl (alexandrite, cat's-eye)	3·71
Turquoise	2·75	Garnet (pyrope)	3·7—3·9
Nephrite	2·99	Garnet (demantoid)	3·85
Tourmaline	3·05	Corundum (ruby and sapphire)	3·99
Spodumene (kunzite, hiddenite)	3·18	Garnet (almandine)	3·9—4·2
Peridot	3·34	Zircon (low type)	4·00
Zoisite (tanzanite)	3·35	Rutile	4·25
Jadeite	3·4	Y.A.G.	4·60
Sinhalite	3·48	Lithium niobate	4·64
Diamond	3·52	Zircon (high type)	4·69
Sphene	3·53	Strontium titanate	5·13

LIGHT

TRULY, without light there could be no world as we know it. No beauty of the sea and sky and no sight of the glorious colours of the flowers in the field, or of the beauty of the precious minerals which are termed gems. Light, however, to the student of gemmology has a more vital interest even than that of beauty—the value it possesses as a means for gem identification.

What is light? That it is the physical cause of our sensation of sight is obvious, just as we may say that it is simply an effect interpreted by our brain through the medium of the eye and has no real existence, but, of its nature, even with the advanced state of science to-day, we are uncertain.

In the year 1666, Sir Isaac Newton suggested that light was due to streams of infinitesimally small particles projected in all directions in straight lines from the luminous body that gave the light. The particles were supposed to be able to penetrate transparent substances, and when they struck upon the retina of the eye to give the sensation of vision. This was called the *emission* or *corpuscular* theory of light.

While this theory was then regarded as quite adequate, as time went on it was found to be insufficient to account for many of the phenomena of light, and was superseded by the *wave* or *undulatory* theory. A clear statement of this theory was given by the Dutch physicist Huyghens, in 1678, in which it is supposed that light consists of some kind of waves coming from a luminous source. For light to have a wave form it seems essential for it to proceed through some sort of medium (*the term "medium" is used to express any substance through which light passes, and may refer to either solids, liquids or gases*). When the light source is that of a candle, gas flame or electric light, the atmosphere may appear to be that medium, but, if we consider that great natural producer of light energy, the sun, the position is different. The sun is 93,000,000 miles away and the earth's atmosphere extends to some 200 to 300 miles above its surface, beyond which there is space, containing, as far as we know, nothing but a few atoms per cubic yard.

In order to support the theory there must be some kind of medium to transfer the wave motion, hence, some scientists assume the existence of a hypothetical medium which is elastic and weightless and is termed *the ether* which pervades all material bodies as well. This theory supposes that wave motion is propagated by successive parts of the ether setting each other in motion by mutually attractive forces. This idea was later modified by the work of James Clerk Maxwell, who suggested that the vibrations were due to periodic alterations in the electrical and magnetic condition of the ether. This is known as the *electro-magnetic theory*.

The conception of light energy was again altered during recent years by a suggestion that the original corpuscular theory was set aside too hastily, and that the various phenomena in connection with light cannot be wholly explained on the basis of the wave theory alone. However, for the study of gems, the wave theory satisfactorily explains practically all the light phenomena which it is necessary to deal with.

Unlike the waves which are produced when a stone is thrown into water, causing the water surface to vibrate in paths at right angles to the surface only, termed *transverse* waves, the waves of light move in all possible directions at right angles to the direction of travel, termed *spherical* waves. The length of these waves is the nearest distance measured between two particles on the wave surface in identically the same position and travelling in the same direction. The intensity of the energy (light) is determined by the amplitude (fig. 22).

White light, or as it is often termed *mixed* light, is composed of a mixture of red, orange, yellow, green, blue, indigo and violet light rays, each of which have a different wave-length. Therefore, the colour of light varies with, and depends upon, the wave-length. Red waves have the longest wave-length and this diminishes through orange, yellow, green, blue to violet, which has the least wave-length and about half the length of the red rays. When light is produced which has one wave-length only it is then termed *monochromatic* light.

When energy has a shorter wave-length than the violet rays, and is therefore invisible, they are termed *ultra-violet* rays, while below the

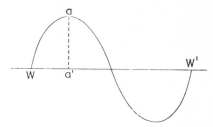

FIG. 22.—Wave form. $W - W^1 =$ wavelength.
$a - a^1 =$ amplitude.

ultra-violet there are those radiations, discovered by Röntgen in 1895, known as X-rays. Still shorter rays are those emitted by radium and termed *gamma* rays and the shortest yet known to science are the *cosmic* rays now being investigated by scientists all the world over. Similarly, at the other end of the scale there are those invisible rays of longer wave-length than the red rays. They are termed the *infra-red* rays and are, in fact, heat rays. Finally, far beyond these heat rays come the rays with the comparatively long wave-lengths of anything from a few metres to something like 2,000 metres. They are the so-called *Herzian* waves, more familiar to us as "wireless." The whole range of these waves produces what is known as the *electro-magnetic spectrum*. In the centre of this spectrum lies that very small octave, the range which affects our eyes, visible light (fig. 23).

The lengths of light waves are so small that measurement by ordinary standards, such as centimetres, is most inconvenient, for instance, the wave-length of the yellow ray (the D_1 line of sodium) is 0·00005896 centimetre. It becomes more understandable if it is expressed as a multiple of a ten-millionth part of a millimetre, a unit advocated by A. J. Angstrom in 1868, and universally adopted. The wave-length of the yellow ray is then 5,896. *Angstrom units* or *angstroms* (generally written A, or the Swedish Å.)

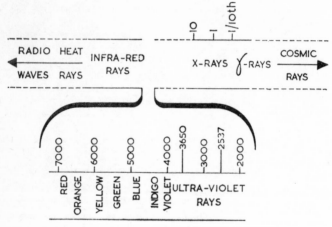

FIG. 23.—The electro-magnetic spectrum.

All the qualities which go to make up the beauty of precious stones are directly due to the powerful influences which they exert upon reflected and transmitted light. The first quality to be considered is *transparency*, which is the ability of a substance to transmit light. It is roughly divided into degrees of transparency as follows:

TRANSPARENT.—An object viewed through them shows outlines clear and distinct; *e.g.* most gemstones, such as diamond, spinel, emerald, etc.

SEMI-TRANSPARENT.—Object would be blurred, but considerable light can penetrate the stone; *e.g.* white chalcedony.

TRANSLUCENT.—Some light passes through but no object can be seen; *e.g.* opal.

SEMI-TRANSLUCENT.—Light only transmitted well through the edges; *e.g.* chrysoprase.

OPAQUE.—No light passes through; *e.g.* lapis lazuli.

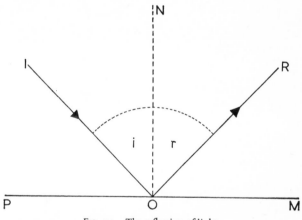

FIG. 24.—The reflection of light.

The above description is considered to refer to specimens of ordinary thickness, for even the opaque substances are translucent if ground to thin sections. Colour will also diminish the effect as will feathers, flaws and fibrous inclusions.

Before considering the other qualities of gemstones in relation to light, it will be as well to discuss the action of light rays when they impinge upon a medium, or from one medium into another.

When a ray of light impinges upon a mirror or other polished surface (say, that of a gemstone), the ray is turned back at the point of incidence (*the point where the ray strikes the surface of the two media in contact*) in a direction opposite to the direction in which it arrives, and at a similar angle, *i.e.* similarly to the manner in which a ball returns when it is thrown at an angle against a wall. This may be explained better by a geometrical example, as fig. 24. PM is a plane reflecting surface. IO a ray of light (the *incident* ray) falling on the mirror at O. O is called the point of incidence. OR is the ray reflected (returned) from the mirror. NO is termed the *normal at the point of incidence* (the *normal* in optics is an imaginary line at right angles to the surface separating the two media at the point where a light ray strikes the separating surface. It is the base line from which all angles made by light rays are measured). The angle ION is the angle of incidence (i). The angle NOR is the angle of reflection (r). The incident ray, IO, the normal, NO, and the reflected ray all lie in the same plane.

The LAWS OF REFLECTION are expressed as follows:

1. The angle of incidence (i) is equal to the angle of reflection (r).
2. The incident ray, the normal and the reflected ray are all in the same plane.

Reflection effects are very important in cut gem stones and have a great deal to do with such properties as lustre and sheen and such effects as asterism (star-stones) and chatoyancy (cat's-eyes).

When a ray of light *enters* a stone (or any medium) in an oblique direction the ray, instead of travelling through the stone in a direct line (that is the straight continuation of the incident ray) is found to alter its course. This bending of the light rays is termed *refraction* and is responsible for such commonly observed facts as the apparent bending of a straight stick when it is partially immersed in water.

For refraction to take place it is necessary for the light to be travelling through media of different optical densities (*not* to be confused with "density" or "specific gravity"). When a ray of light travels from air, an optically rare medium, into a gemstone, an optically denser medium, the refracted ray is bent towards, or nearer to, the normal.

Expressed geometrically (fig. 25), IO is the incident ray, OR the refracted ray, and NN[1] the normal at the point of incidence. It will be seen at once that the angle of incidence (i) ION, is greater than the angle of refraction (r) N[1]OR, and experiment has shown that any

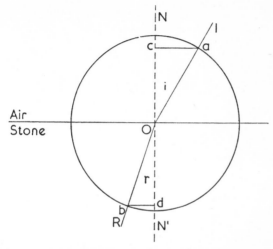

Fig. 25.—Refraction of light. A circle drawn with centre at the point of incidence of the light ray, and with any radius which cuts the incident and refracted rays at a and b respectively, will, when perpendiculars ac and bd are dropped on to the normal, produce right-angled triangles. Therefore the ratio of the side ac and the hypotenuse aO gives the sine of the angle of incidence, and the ratio bd and bO will give the sine of the angle of refraction.

increase, or decrease, in the angle of incidence causes an increase, or decrease, in the angle of refraction, and that this variation is in some definite proportion.

The LAWS OF REFRACTION, attributed to the physicist Snell in the seventeenth century and known as SNELL'S LAW, are expressed as follows:

    1. The sine of the angle of incidence bears to the sine of the angle

of refraction a definite ratio which depends only upon the two media in contact and the nature (colour) of the light, *i.e.*:

$$\frac{\text{Sine } i}{\text{Sine } r} = \text{a constant.}$$

2. The incident ray, the normal at the point of incidence and the refracted ray are all in the same plane.

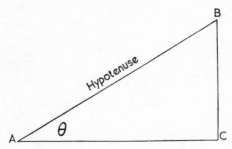

FIG. 26.—In a right-angled triangle the sine of an angle is the ratio between the side opposite the angle and the hypotenuse. That is $\frac{\text{BC}}{\text{AB}}$ is the sine of the angle θ.

In a right-angled triangle the sine of an angle is the ratio between the side opposite the angle and the hypotenuse (the *hypotenuse* is the side of a right-angled triangle opposite the right angle) (fig. 26); hence (refer to fig. 25) if a circle is described with centre at the point of incidence O, and with any radius which cuts the incident and refracted rays at *a* and *b* respectively, perpendiculars *ac* and *bd* dropped on to the normal produce right-angled triangles. Therefore, the ratio of the side *ac* and the hypotenuse *a*O gives the sine of the angle of incidence (the angle *i*), and likewise ratio of the sides *bd* and *a*O give the sine of the angle of refraction (the angle *r*).

From the laws of refraction it will be seen that:

$$\frac{\text{Sine angle of incidence}}{\text{Sine angle of refraction}} = \frac{\text{Sine } i}{\text{Sine } r} = \text{a constant}$$

a constant, which, when a ray of light travels from air to another medium, is termed the *refractive index* of that medium and is a measure of its refractive power. Refractive index (usually termed R.I.) is constant for the same medium, but differs for different substances, *e.g.* the R.I. of water differs from that of, say, Vaseline. However, water always has the same index of refraction and so does all Vaseline. Hence, the constant forms a valuable factor for the discrimination of gem materials.

When dealing with specific gravity, we saw that water is used as the standard or unity. The standard used for refractive index is air (strictly speaking it should be a vacuum, but the difference between air and a vacuum is so small that it is negligible); therefore, the refractive index of air is reckoned as 1. Gemstones are optically denser than air so that their index of refraction is greater than 1. (*Methods whereby the constant of refractive index can be used to differentiate between gems and counterfeits will be discussed in a later lesson.*)

Light is reversible, that is, it may travel from the *denser* medium to the *rarer* medium, *e.g.* from a gemstone into air. Therefore, it will be obvious that the incident ray, now in denser medium, will make a smaller angle with the normal than does the refracted ray which is now in the rarer medium. Considering the case more thoroughly, we will realize that as the angle of refraction increases in ratio with increase of the angle of incidence, there will become an angle of incidence where the refracted ray is at an angle of 90° to the normal. That is, the refracted ray just grazes the surface separating the two media (R3, fig. 27). Any further increase of the angle of incidence causes the ray to turn back into the first, denser, medium (R4, fig. 27), where it obeys the laws of reflection and *not* the law of refraction. This phenomenon is termed *total internal reflection of light*. The angle of incidence which gives an angle of refraction of 90° is termed the *critical angle* and is usually denoted by the Greek letter theta θ. The critical angle determines the beginning of total internal reflection.

Total internal reflection is a property which is made use of in much of the optical apparatus used to-day; examples which may be cited are

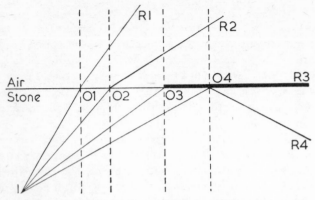

FIG. 27.—Total internal reflection of light.

the various forms of totally reflecting prisms incorporated in such apparatus as submarine periscopes and in prismatic binoculars.

The value of the critical angle may be expressed by the formula:

$$\text{sine } i = \frac{1}{n}$$

where i is the critical angle and n the index of refraction, hence, it

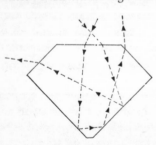

FIG. 28.—Path of light rays in a diamond.

follows that the higher the refractive index the smaller the critical angle. That is, more light will be totally reflected in a medium of high refraction, and this explains the brilliancy of the diamond. Most of the light rays which enter the diamond from the front are totally reflected from the back facets and out again through those at the front (fig. 28).

When a beam of white light is passed through a transparent medium with parallel sides, such as a glass plate, the emergent ray is found to be parallel to the incident ray although often laterally displaced (fig. 29). When, however, a beam of white light is passed through a

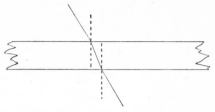

FIG. 29.—Path of light rays through a parallel-sided glass plate.

transparent medium with two inclined faces, such as a glass prism, the ray of white light is resolved into the familiar colours of the rainbow (fig. 30). This resolution is due to the fact that each colour is bent, or deviated, a different amount; that is, the refractive index of a medium differs for each ray and increases regularly with decrease of wavelength.

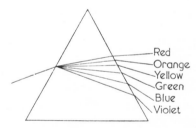

FIG. 30.—Dispersion of light rays passing through a glass prism.

Thus, the prism analyses the beam of white light and arranges the various coloured rays according to their wave-length. The longer waves (red light) are least deviated, while the shorter waves (violet light) are most bent, or are, as it is termed, more *refrangible*. This separation of the rainbow colours, first observed by Newton, is termed *dispersion* and determines the effect known as "fire."

Dispersion or "fire" may be defined as the play of prismatic colours and is strongest in such stones as diamond, rutile and strontium titanate, demantoid and hessonite garnet, sphene and zircon. It is best seen in diamond and colourless stones, for in the others the effect is masked by the colour of the stone.

The amount of dispersion is measured by the difference between the refractive index for the red ray and the refractive index of the violet ray, but in practice it is usual to take what is known as the B and G lines of the spectrum (*spectrum* is the name applied to the spread of rainbow colours) which have wave-lengths of 6,867 angstroms and 4,308 angstroms, respectively. The dispersion of diamond for the different coloured rays is as follows:

$$
\begin{aligned}
\text{Red} \quad & (6{,}870 \text{ A}) = 2 \cdot 407 \text{ n} \\
\text{Yellow} \quad & (5{,}890 \text{ A}) = 2 \cdot 417 \text{ n} \\
\text{Green} \quad & (5{,}270 \text{ A}) = 2 \cdot 427 \text{ n} \\
\text{Violet} \quad & (3{,}970 \text{ A}) = 2 \cdot 465 \text{ n} \\
& (\text{n} = \text{refractive index})
\end{aligned}
$$

This gives the amount of the dispersion between the red and the violet rays of 0·058. Between the B and G lines the dispersion of diamond is 0·045.

The *fundamental* colour of a medium (gemstone) is caused by the absorption of certain wave-lengths (colours) from the white light falling upon it, thus causing the residual colours (those *not* absorbed) to give a colour to the medium. In opaque stones this absorption takes place at or near the surface, and in transparent stones the absorption takes place when the light is passing through the stone. Light passing through a ruby has the orange, yellow, green and violet absorbed from the spectrum; hence, the red and some blue are transmitted, which together give the typical ruby colour. This effect causing colour is termed *selective absorption of light*.

Colour may also be produced by what is known as *interference*. If a ray of light impinges on a thin film, such as a soap bubble, AB in fig. 31, part of the ray is reflected along BC and part BD refracted into the medium (thin film), where it is reflected along DE and out along EF. BC and EF are parallel and close together, but EF will be retarded owing to its longer passage along BDE. Hence, if the incident light is white some of the wave-lengths will be half a wave-length different. That is, out of phase (the crest of one wave will fill the trough of one in the other set, thus destroying light of that colour) leaving the complementary spectrum colours visible to the eye, colours which differ according to the angle at which the surface is viewed.

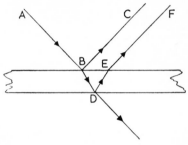

FIG. 31.—Interference of light at a thin film.

Colour may also be produced by interference due to diffraction where structures in a mineral, or artificially formed as in a diffraction grating, can cause new sets of light vibrations to be formed which interfere with one another. Both phase interference and interference by diffraction may be the cause of colour in pearl, opal and some other gem materials.

The appearance of a stone in reflected light is termed its *lustre* and is mainly a function of its R.I., its structure and transparency. While in no way is it suggested to be related with hardness, hardness must have some influence in determining the polish, and polish does have some influence on lustre. It must be remembered, too, that a ray of light incident on a stone must suffer both refraction and reflection simultaneously in some degree. This also may affect the kind of lustre. Lustre is known as *adamantine* in those stones of high R.I., such as diamond and zircon, while most gemstones have a lustre described as *vitreous* or glass-like; *resinous* is the type shown by amber, some opals and hessonite garnet. *Silky* lustre is seen in fibrous stones, such as satin-spar, while *pearly* is typical of mother-of-pearl. *Dull* lustre is that seen on many opaque stones, as turquoise, while *greasy* is the type seen in soap-stone. Certain opaque minerals, such as marcasite and pyrites, gold and silver, etc., have a *metallic* lustre.

In contradistinction to lustre, *sheen* is due to reflection from within the stone and is termed *opalescence* when the reflections consist of milky or pearly reflections, *e.g.* moonstone. The cat's-eye effect, known as *chatoyancy*, is due to reflections from parallel fibrous cavities within the stone, which, when the stone is cut *en cabochon* (that is with a dome-shaped top), show a single wavy band of light which moves as the stone is turned. The band of light is at right angles to the direction of the fibres and may be likened to the band of light seen on a reel of silk. Should the fibres run in three directions, such as in some ruby and sapphire, and occasionally in rose quartz, where the fibres run in three directions parallel to the lateral axes of the hexagonal system a six-rayed star of light is produced provided the stone is cut with the base in the same plane as the lateral axes. This effect is termed *asterism*, and the stones are known as star-stones.

In all the phenomena that have so far been discussed, light has been assumed to travel through all media as one ray. This is not always so. In material in which light does travel as one ray, the material is said to be *singly refracting* or *isotropic*. Such materials are amorphous substances, as glasses, resins and all liquids; and all crystals of the cubic system. In the other crystal systems the incident ray is split into two rays which take different paths within the stone. That is, they have differing refractive indices. Such material is termed *doubly refractive* or *anisotropic*, and the effect is well seen in the variety of calcium carbonate known as *Iceland spar*. Print viewed through the spar is seen to be doubled.

In doubly refractive stones there are either one or two directions parallel to which light suffers no double refraction; these are termed *optic axes*, and are perhaps better defined as directions of single refraction in a doubly refractive stone. The tetragonal, hexagonal and trigonal systems have one optic axis, which is parallel to the principal crystal axis. Crystals of these systems are said to be *uniaxial*. Crystals of the other three systems, the rhombic, monoclinic and triclinic systems, have two optic axes, which do not necessarily show a relation to the crystal axes; hence, these crystals are termed *biaxial*.

In uniaxial stones one of the rays has a refractive index which is constant and independent of the direction of the ray. It obeys the ordinary laws of refraction and is termed the *ordinary* ray, and is usually denoted by the letter *o*, or by the Greek letter *omega* = ω. The other ray, termed the *extraordinary* ray, has a refractive index which varies from that of the ordinary ray to a second limiting value. The extraordinary ray is denoted by the letter *e*, or by the Greek letter *epilson* = ε. If the extraordinary ray has an index of refraction greater than that for the ordinary ray, the *sign* of double refraction is said to be *positive*, if less, *negative*.

In biaxial stones there are still only two rays travelling in any one direction, but there are three critical values for the refractive index. One corresponding to rays vibrating parallel to the line bisecting the acute angle between the optic axes (*acute bisectrix*); one corresponding to rays vibrating parallel to the line bisecting the obtuse angle between the optic axes (*obtuse bisectrix*); and the other, an intermediate index, corresponding to rays in which the vibration is at right angles to the other two. These three indices are denoted by α (the least), β (the intermediate), and γ (the greatest). When the greatest index (*gamma* = γ) is the acute bisectrix, the stone is said to be positive in sign. When the least index (*alpha* = α) is the acute bisectrix the sign is negative. The sign of biaxial stones may also be shown by the difference in magnitude of the three indices of refraction. When the intermediate index (*beta* = β) is nearer to α than it is to γ, the stone is positive, and when nearer to γ than to α, the stone is negative.

Example.

| Topaz | $a = 1 \cdot 607$, | $\beta = 1 \cdot 610$, | $\gamma = 1 \cdot 618$. |
| Epidote | $= 1 \cdot 730$, | $= 1 \cdot 754$, | $= 1 \cdot 768$. |

Therefore, topaz is positive and epidote is negative.

Birefringence is the term used for the strength of the double refraction, that is, the difference between the indices ω and ε in uniaxial stones and between a and γ in biaxial stones.

Example.

| Quartz | $\varepsilon = 1 \cdot 553$, $\omega = 1 \cdot 544$ *(birefringence = $\cdot 009$)* |
| Topaz | $\gamma = 1 \cdot 618$, $a = 1 \cdot 607$ *(birefringence = $\cdot 011$)* |

By the use of a lens gemstones with large birefringence, such as peridot (0·038), zircon (0·059), the double refraction is apparent by the doubling of the edges of the back facets when viewed through the stone (provided the view is not taken along a direction of single refraction, an optic axis). This test is useful with colourless zircon, which sometimes simulates diamond (diamond is a cubic mineral and hence is singly refractive). Experience will show that the doubling of the rear facets may be seen even with stones of low birefringence, but in the case of topaz it may not be readily apparent owing to the shift being lateral, one edge overlapping the other and parallel to it, so the double effect is not seen.

Previously it has been stated that a ray of light vibrates in all directions at right angles to the direction of travel. While this is true for light rays reaching the eye from a light source, when the ray enters a doubly refractive stone and is split into two rays, the vibrations take place in each ray only in one definite direction in the plane at right angles to the direction of travel. This is termed *plane polarized* light, or simply *polarized* light. The two rays in doubly refractive stones are plane polarized in directions at right angles to each other. This effect has a very definite use in gem testing and will be dealt with again when discussing methods for the production of light having this quality.

MEASUREMENT OF REFRACTIVE INDEX

It will be recalled that in the last lesson, refractive index was stated to be a *constant*, and that it forms a valuable testing factor. How, then, may this constant be measured in order to be of use for differentiating between gemstones? Actually there are several methods whereby this may be accomplished, all of which have, in general, some limit to their usefulness. In the discussion of the different methods which follows no attempt has been made to group them in chronological order, but simply in order of suggested usefulness.

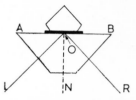

Fig. 32.—Schematic diagram of a dense glass prism of a refractometer showing the path of the ray at the point of the critical angle of total internal reflection.

Of prime importance to the gemmologist is the method whereby use is made of a special optical instrument termed a *refractometer*, or, as it is sometimes called, a *total reflectometer*. These instruments measure the critical angle of total reflection, or as is more usual in the ordinary commercial type of instruments, show on a scale calibrated in indices of refraction the shadow edge of this angle.

The essential feature of the instrument is a hemisphere or prism of, usually, a very dense and highly refractive glass. Fig. 32 represents a section through such a glass upon which is resting the stone under test (*which must have a refractive index less than that of the glass*). The ray IO passes through the dense glass and strikes the surface AB at the critical angle ION for the stone and the glass. This ray IO will then be totally reflected and, hence, returned along OR. All the rays penetrating the dense glass between A and I will be totally reflected through the area

B—R, which must be in consequence much lighter than the area R—N, because all rays entering the dense glass between I and N do so at an angle less than the critical angle and, therefore, are refracted out and lost through the stone. The position of the bounding edge at R, between the comparatively light and the comparatively dark areas, is a measure of the critical angle of the two media (dense glass and stone) in contact. Assuming that, and it is obvious that it would be in the case

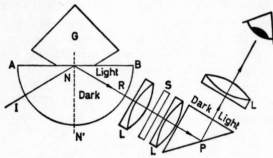

FIG. 33.—The path of the light ray at the critical angle in the optical system of a refractometer.

of an instrument, the same dense glass is used, any stone having, say, an R.I. of 1·72, will have the shadow edge at a different position from that of a stone with an R.I. of 1·45. If, then, a lens system and eyepiece, complete with scale, arranged so that the shadow edge can be read, is placed in conjunction with the dense glass we have, in fact, a refractometer (see fig. 33).

So far it has been comparatively plain sailing, but, there are some special factors which have not yet been considered, and must be dealt with before going on to the types of instruments available. These are, in general, limiting factors. That is, they preclude the ability of the instrument being used to read indices of high refraction. As should be now quite clear, to obtain total internal reflections it is necessary for the light ray to be travelling from an optically denser medium to one which is optically rarer, hence, any gem stone which has a higher R.I. than the dense glass hemisphere or prism will not return the rays back into the glass by total reflection, but will allow the light to go out through the stone, therefore the scale will be uniformly dark. There have been constructed special types of refractometers made with dense "glasses" of zinc blende and diamond (R.I.'s, 2·37 and 2·42 respectively). The indices for the dense optical glasses used in the ordinary instruments will be given for each instrument as it is discussed; however, in no case does it exceed 1·90.

The second point to consider is that when a clean stone is placed on a clean dense glass of a refractometer a film of air remains between them and prevents *optical contact*. To displace this film a liquid, which will *wet* the glass and the stone, has to be placed between them. This liquid, of necessity, has to have a higher index of refraction than the stone under test, and it is the difficulty of the preparation of such liquids which causes the second limiting factor. There are two qualities necessary for such a liquid—a high index of refraction and the fact that it will *wet* both stone and dense glass. A list of liquids suitable, in varying degree, for use as a contact liquid is now appended.

1. MONOBROMONAPHTHALENE, R.I. = 1·66 (*too low for general use*).
2. METHYLENE IODIDE, R.I. = 1·74 (*no use for corundum gems*).
3. METHYLENE IODIDE, with dissolved SULPHUR, R.I. = 1·79.
4. METHYLENE IODIDE with SULPHUR and C_2I_4, R.I. = 1·81.
5. PHENYLDI-IODOARSINE, R.I. = 1·85. A poisonous, blistering fluid.
6. WEST'S SOLUTION (eight parts of yellow phosphorus with one part of methylene iodide and one part of recrystallized sulphur), R.I. = 2·05. Spontaneously inflammable unless carefully handled.
7. SELENIUM BROMIDE with a drop of the 1·81 (No. 4) liquid gives readings up to 1·95. Selenium bromide is a dark fluid with a very high refractive index. This fluid, which dissociates upon contact with the air, can be made by the direct reaction between selenium and bromine under concentrated sulphuric acid. It is mixed with the other liquid, which lowers its R.I., in order to give it the necessary "wetting" quality.

It will now be apparent that these two limiting factors taken in conjunction, preclude a reading being taken for diamond. On the usual instruments, which combine a glass hemisphere and "normal" liquids (normal liquids are those numbered 3 and 4 in the list) the gems diamond, zircon, sphene, demantoid garnet, strontium titanate and rutile will only give a *negative* reading, that is, the whole of the scale, up to the edge given by the liquid, appears dark. It must also be pointed out that the specimen under test must have a flat polished facet, hence, only by a special technique can the refractive index of stones with curved surfaces be obtained.

When a stone, such as a spinel, is in position on the dense glass of a refractometer, with a suitable contact liquid between the stone and the glass, and the scale is viewed through the eyepiece, the observer sees the lower half (that is the part of the scale with lower readings up to 1·72) dark, and the higher readings comparatively light. The shadow edge of reading 1·72 is the reading for the stone, and if a careful observation is made it will be seen that there is another edge higher in the scale due to the contact liquid used. Turning again to the shadow edge at 1·72 (for spinel) it will be seen that this edge is in reality a small spectrum in which the red end is in the bright portion of the field and the violet merges into the dark part. In making this statement it is assumed that, as in ordinary general testing it would, the refractometer is used in daylight or ordinary artificial light. The coloured edge is due to the relative dispersions of the stone and the glass. Refractometer glasses have a very high dispersion. If the glass hemisphere and the stone under test had similar dispersions the shadow edge would not be coloured, and one type of instrument has been constructed with a "glass" which will do this. It will be discussed later. However, a shadow edge which is sharp and not coloured may be obtained by the use of *monochromatic light*, which, as has been mentioned in the lesson on "Light," is light of one wave-length (colour) only. The standard monochromatic light for refractometer use is the yellow light of sodium. The majority of the figures given for refractive indices are for the yellow ray and also all refractometers are calibrated on this ray. Sodium light can be easily obtained by burning in the hot part of a bunsen flame any compound containing sodium, such as common salt (NaCl) or sodium carbonate (Na_2CO_3), which is perhaps better known as washing soda. An ordinary spirit flame can be used to produce the light by similar means, but for the finest results there is nothing to beat the electric sodium discharge lamp for brilliant production of sodium light. These lamps are somewhat expensive.

So far, singly refractive media alone have been discussed. Doubly refractive stones, when examined on a refractometer, show not *one* shadow edge but *two* such edges, whose actual position will vary according to the orientation of the stone. On the stone being carefully rotated on the dense glass it will be seen that in certain positions the edges attain maximum and minimum positions. These two readings show the minimum and maximum indices for the stone, and if the figure for the minimum reading is subtracted from the figure of the maximum reading the difference is the amount of double refraction (*birefringence*) of the stone. It must be remembered that all singly refractive stones can only show a single shadow edge and if two edges are seen the stone must be doubly refractive. With stones of weak birefringence it is practically impossible to detect the two edges when white light is used and monochromatic light is then a necessity. The *amount* of double refraction is often of great value in determining between stones of similar refractive indices; care should be taken, however, not to read the edge due to the contact liquid for the higher edge of a stone.

An alternative method whereby the existence of double refraction may be determined on a refractometer is by placing over the eyepiece a nicol prism or other apparatus arranged for the production of plane polarized light. The rays corresponding to the two refractive indices in a doubly refracting stone are vibrating at right angles to one another, the "polar" (nicol prism or "polaroid" disc) only allows light to pass which is vibrating parallel to a certain direction, hence, by turning the "polar" to the correct position only the shadow edge due to one ray can be seen, and on rotating the prism through 90°,

the other ray can be seen. If the stone is singly refracting there will
be no change in reading however the prism is turned, whereas, if the
stone is doubly refracting two different readings, a minimum and
maximum, are obtained when the prism is turned through a right
angle.

To use the refractometer, the instrument should be placed in a
position where light from a window or table lamp can enter the
instrument. A drop of the highly refractive contact liquid is placed on
the centre of the dense glass, which should have been wiped clean
with a piece of clean blotting paper. The stone, after being cleaned
also (a clean stone is a necessity), is now placed with its table facet
down on the dense glass and liquid. The scale is then viewed through
the eyepiece. If the scale is not in focus, this may be corrected by the
adjustment of the eyepiece. As before mentioned the scale will be seen
to be part dark, and part light. Watching the most prominent shadow
edge, that of the stone (the other edge, due to the liquid, is weak, and
is nearly at the end of the scale), the stone is rotated to see if there is
any separation of the edge into two, and, if so, to their maximum
separation. Monochromatic light is in all probability necessary if the
amount of double refraction is small. Fig. 36 shows the scale of a
Tully instrument as it would appear when (a) a spinel, (b) a topaz,
(c) a tourmaline is the stone being tested. The full birefringence can
be obtained on any one facet by turning the stone and taking the
maximum and minimum readings. In uniaxial stones the full birefringence can be seen when the difference between the shadow edges
is at its greatest; with biaxial stones, however, as both edges move it
is necessary to read the lower edge at its lowest, and then ignoring this
edge to turn the stone until the upper edge is at its highest in order
to obtain the full birefringence.

The refractive index of stones with curved surfaces may be obtained
with some accuracy by using the distant vision or spot-contact
method devised by Lester Benson of America. To do this a small drop
of contact liquid is applied to the centre of the dense glass of the
refractometer and then to hold the curved surface of the stone on the

spot of liquid and in contact with the surface of the dense glass. With the eye withdrawn to about 15 inches away from the eyepiece it will be seen that a small disc is visible in the field. On moving the eye in an up and down direction this small disc will change from being fully dark at low readings and fully light at high readings. At some intermediate position between the two (providing the stone has an index within the range) the disc will be seen to be bisected by a line of shadow. When this position is found the eye must be lowered towards the eyepiece so that the previously out of focus scale can be read. The method requires practice, the two edges of doubly refractive stones can rarely be seen, and the readings are often about two points low. The method is useful also for small stones with tiny table facets.

Bright-line readings accomplished by removing the cover from the Rayner refractometer, blocking up the normal light window (possibly with a matchbox) and letting the light come from just above the top of the dense glass will provide measurements in those cases impossible with orthodox methods. This is useful for "bloomed" stones and some pastes which do not give satisfactory readings.

The HERBERT SMITH REFRACTOMETER was first brought out in 1905, and was designed by Dr. G. F. Herbert Smith, as an improvement on an earlier instrument made by E. Bertrand. The scale was not calibrated in indices of refraction but just in a series of equal spaced and numbered divisions, each instrument being separately calibrated. A card supplied with the instrument had a written table showing what each scale number of that particular instrument represented in terms of R.I. About 1907, the Herbert Smith refractometer was re-designed to its present form complete with a scale calibrated directly in terms of refractive indices (fig. 34). It is essentially a hand instrument fitted with a sliced hemisphere of dense glass which will allow readings to be taken up to the limit of the scale, which is 1·790. On this instrument no cover is fitted to keep light away from the top of the stone and dense glass when readings are being taken, it being intended that the hand used to rotate the stone should perform this duty. Fig. 33

shows the optical arrangement of the Herbert Smith instrument. It is
suggested that the best way to use the instrument is to place the
refractometer on a book before a piece of white matt paper, such as
blotting paper, the whole lay-out being placed in front of a table lamp
so arranged that the light is reflected up and into the instrument.

FIG. 34.—The Herbert Smith refractometer and the scale of the instrument.

The TULLY REFRACTOMETER was the first instrument which may be
said to have broken away from tradition in design. A product of the
years after the First World War, it was designed in 1925 by the late
Bristow G. Tully in conjunction with Mr. J. Pike, the technical expert
to Messrs. Rayner & Keeler, Ltd. It is not now made. Essentially a
table instrument (fig. 35), its large and comparatively heavy base
precludes the likelihood of damage through inadvertence to which
a smaller instrument would be prone. The other prominent feature
of this instrument is the full hemisphere of dense glass which is
mounted in a metal collar and allows the glass to be rotated by the
finger. This avoids the liability of damage to the soft dense glass
which is likely when the stone is turned on the dense glass by hand.
The scale is clear and brilliant and reads up to 1·86 (special models
were made which read up to 1·90). Unlike other refractometers the
scale of the Tully is erect (fig. 36), that is, the scale reads from the
bottom to the top. A hinged reflector directs the light on to the

hemisphere and a convenient cover protects the specimen from top light during an examination.

A - REFLECTOR.
B - DENSE GLASS HEMISPHERE.
C - GEM UNDER TEST.
D - VELVET LINED SCREEN.
F. H & J - LENSES.
G & I - PRISMS.
K - SCALE

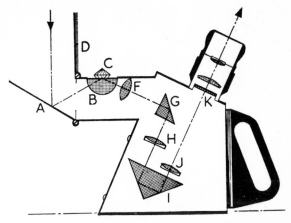

FIG. 35.—The Tully refractometer.

The RAYNER REFRACTOMETER was brought out in 1936. It has a certain similarity of design to the Smith instrument, but with an ingenious system of truncated lenses and prisms the instrument is made so flat that it takes up little more room than would a stone wallet. There is no hemisphere, the dense glass being made in the form of a small prism, this makes a very small table which, however, is in some ways an advantage. The scale of the Rayner, unlike the Tully, is inverted. It reads to 1·86. There is a top light cover and an exceptionally quick-acting focusing device to the eyepiece. No light reflector is necessary with this instrument so none is provided. Like

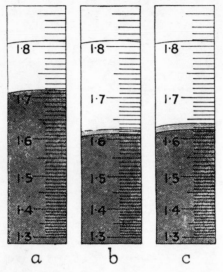

FIG. 36.—Scale of the Tully refractometer. a, reading shown by a singly refractive stone (reading is that of a natural spinel). b, reading shown by a doubly refractive stone (reading that of topaz). c as b, but showing greater separation of the shadow edges, *e.g.*, tourmaline (readings as seen when monochromatic light is used).

the Tully, the Rayner is a product of Rayners. The design of the Rayner refractometer, which is the standard and most common refractometer met today, has been altered to a more stable pattern (fig. 37).

A new type of Rayner refractometer, the DIALDEX, dispenses with the scale and the shadow edges are seen on a plain field, the measurement of the refractive indices being made by turning a drum dial at the side of the instrument. This dial is marked in refractive indices and on turning it a black "ribbon" is seen to travel down the "field" and the lower edge of this is put into juxtaposition with the shadow edges and the indices are then read off on the dial. The advantages of this instrument is that the scale on the drum is relatively much wider and allows for easier reading on the third place of decimals, and, further, the glass used has less dispersion so that it is possible to read the two edges of doubly refractive stones in ordinary white light.

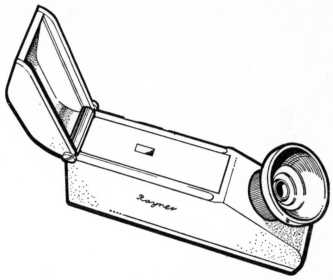

FIG. 37.—The Rayner refractometer.

The ANDERSON-PAYNE SPINEL model of the RAYNER REFRACTOMETER has the same optical arrangement as the ordinary Rayner instrument, but in place of a dense glass prism there is a prism of synthetic white spinel. The function of this instrument, which will read up to about 1·66, is to make easy reading of those gemstones, and they are by far the majority, which have indices below this value. The dispersions of the white spinel and most gemstones are very similar, so that in ordinary white light the shadow edges, even in weakly birefringement stones, can be quite clearly seen. Also most pastes will, owing to their high dispersion, show a wide spectrum shadow edge on this instrument, and by this means may be identified.

The ANDERSON-PAYNE DIAMOND model of the RAYNER REFRACTO-METER has a dense "glass" made of a diamond. It has a scale which extends from 1·55 to 2·05, so long that the eyepiece is made to run on a track so that any desired part of the scale can be viewed. With this instrument, in order to utilize the high range, it is necessary to use either of the highly refractive liquids, such as West's solution or selenium bromide. It is recommended that sodium light be used. A similar instrument has been made which uses for the prism the mineral zinc blende.

It may be an advantage to give a few hints on the care of refractometers. In the instruments which have a hemisphere of dense glass, this hemisphere is very soft, far softer than are the gemstones which are placed upon it, hence it is essential to ensure that the polished surface is not scratched by careless placing of the gemstone on the table. Corn-tongs should be used to place and centre the stones whenever possible. Liquid should be carefully removed after the refractometer has been in use (many of the contact liquids have a detrimental effect if left for long on the glass). Blotting paper is best to clean and absorb the liquid from the glass. Before putting the instrument away after use the dense glass should be wiped and then smeared with a film of Vaseline. Occasionally the glass table should be gently polished with a clean leather and jewellers' rouge.

For good results—

Don't spoil the polish of the glass hemisphere.
Don't try and get a reading with a dirty stone.
Don't put your instrument away in a dirty condition.

The use of the refractometer is the jeweller's most important method of refractive index determination, but, as has been mentioned before, is not the only method whereby this constant can be measured, some of these other methods do have, at times, a practical use in the discrimination of gemstones.

The METHOD OF MINIMUM DEVIATION is one of great accuracy. It requires the use of an expensive instrument, the spectrometer, and is a method for use in the laboratory only, hence, will not be discussed at length. It must be mentioned that this method is the only accurate one whereby the values of dispersion may be found. It is carried out by obtaining the refractive index for the red ray and the blue ray using monochromatic coloured lights. The difference in the values giving the dispersion. The DIRECT MEASUREMENT or, as it is termed, DUC de CHAULNES' METHOD, is useful for specimens which have two parallel sides, such as a small octahedron of diamond, or even the top or table facet and the culet (the small facet at the base of a cut stone and parallel to the table) in a brilliant cut stone. If one of these parallel surfaces is placed on a glass slide on the stage of a measuring or petrological microscope fitted with a calibrated fine adjustment and the microscope is focused on to the uppermost of the two parallel faces, a reading is made. A second reading is made when the microscope is focused on to the lower face as viewed through the specimen. The difference between these two readings gives the apparent depth of the specimen. Then, by pushing the glass slide along and focusing the microscope on to its surface and taking a reading, we are able, by ascertaining the difference between this reading and the reading of the top face, to calculate the real depth of the stone. The simple calculation:

$$\frac{\text{real depth}}{\text{apparent depth}}$$

gives the refractive index. The method has little practical value.

BECKE'S METHOD is useful when small fragments may be chipped from the specimen, such as may be possible from the base of a carved figure.

The chip is first of all placed on a microscope slide with a drop of liquid of known R.I. (*any of the liquids named as contact liquids for refractometer use are applicable. They may be reduced to any R.I. by dilution with one lower in the scale, e.g. methylene iodide may be diluted with monobromonaphthalene*). The slide is placed on the stage of a microscope and the chip accurately focused. On raising the microscope tube from the position of exact focus, a white line is seen at the margin of the specimen and liquid, which travels into the medium of higher refraction. Hence, whether the index of the specimen is higher or lower than the liquid of known index, or between two such liquids, may be easily determined.

A modification of the Becke test which had been noted independently by Schlossmacher and by Mitchell, is as follows: With the diaphragm half-closed and the sub-stage condenser of the microscope lowered, the stone is immersed, table facet down, in a cell of liquid of known refractive index and placed on the microscope stage. When the focus of the microscope is in the liquid above the stone, if the stone has a higher index than the liquid the facet edges will appear white, and on lowering the focus into the stone the facet edges will turn black. With stones of lower refractive index the reverse effect is seen.

The IMMERSION METHOD is useful where small stones are not easily "get-atable," for example: a cluster ring contains some white stones which may be diamonds or synthetic white sapphires or spinels. The method is based on the fact that when a specimen is immersed in a liquid having a similar refractive index to itself the relief is low, i.e. the edges tend to disappear. Readers will recall that is is this phenomenon which is used as a basis by H. G. Wells in his fantasy, The Invisible Man. To put the method into practice, the specimen is immersed in one liquid after another until one is found in which it most completely disappears. It is then known that the specimen must have a refractive index approximating to that of the liquid. Should the position be, as quoted in the example of the ring above—where it is required to know whether the stones are diamonds or one of the synthetic white gems—it is not necessary to obtain an accurate approximation between the liquid and stones, for, if the ring is immersed in a small cell, preferably of white china or else standing on a white surface, containing monobromonaphthalene or methylene iodide, the stones, if diamonds, would stand out in high relief and, if either of the synthetics, low relief.

The IMMERSION CONTRAST METHOD devised by B. W. Anderson

must be mentioned. In this method the stone/s are immersed in a liquid of known refractive index which is contained in a glass-bottomed cell. This cell with the stone and liquid is held above a white paper and illuminated by an overhead light. The images of the stones on the white paper will show that those with a higher index than the liquid will have dark borders and white facet edges; and conversely those of lower index will show white borders and dark facet edges. A coloured edge will indicate a near approach in refractive index of the liquid and stone. Further, the greater the width of the border, either light or dark, will indicate that the stones are near or far from the index of the liquid. Thus some assessment may be made of the index of the stone. A slow photographic film placed below the glass cell will allow a permanent record to be made of the effect, but, unless the film is printed on to photographic paper the lights and darks will be reversed.

Below is appended a short list of the refractive indices of the principal gemstones. Doubly refractive stones are shown with their maximum and minimum indices of refraction.

			Refractive Index.		Birefringence.
Fluorspar ...	...	...		1·43	—
Opal ...	...	...		1·45	—
Feldspar ...	...	...	1·53	1·54	·005
Quartz ...	...	...	1·54	1·55	·009
Synthetic emerald		...	1·56	1·56	·003
Beryl ...	...	...	1·57	1·58	·006
Topaz ...	...	...	1·62	1·63	·008
Tourmaline	...	...	1·62	1·64	·018
Andalusite...	...	...	1·63	1·64	·010
Spodumene	...	...	1·66	1·68	·015
Peridot ...	...	...	1·65	1·69	·038
Zoisite ...	...	...	1·69	1·70	·009
Spinel ...	...	...		1·72	—
Chrysoberyl	...	...	1·74	1·75	·009
Hessonite Garnet ...		...		1·74	—
Pyrope Garnet	...	...		1·75	—
Corundum	...	...	1·76	1·77	·008

Spessartite Garnet	....		1·80	—
Almandine Garnet	...		1·81	—
Y.A.G.	...		1·83	—
Demantoid Garnet	...		1·89	—
Sphene	...	1·90	2·02	·115
Zircon	...	1·93	1·99	·059
Lithium niobate ...	...	2·21	2·30	·090
Strontium titanate	...		2·41	—
Diamond	...		2·42	—
Synthetic rutile ...	...	2·62	2·90	·287

Pyrope garnet intermixes by isomorphous replacement with almandine garnet; thus a series of garnets having a refractive index of any value between 1·75 and 1·81 may be found.

Glass (paste stones) may have any refractive index, but are usually between 1·50 and 1·70; thus, as there are few singly refractive natural stones between these values, a stone giving a singly refractive reading between these values should give suspicion that it is a paste.

Recently a new type of gem-testing instrument based on the relation to index of refraction to Fresnel reflectance. These instruments, which are sold by a number of American manufacturers, do not use visible light but infra-red "light" of about one micron in wavelength. They do not measure birefringence and are not as accurate as the optical refractometers, but they can give a reading for stones above 1·80, the readings being on a suitably marked micro-ammeter. An interesting point is that on these instruments, owing to the differences in dispersion of the stone in the infra-red region, strontium titanate gives a lower reading than diamond, so one can be identified from the other.

COLOUR IN GEM DISTINCTION

IN most transparent gemstones colour is an accidental quality and, in general, gemstones are colourless when in the pure state; for example, pure corundum (oxide of aluminium) is colourless (white sapphire), but when containing a very small percentage of the oxide of the metal chromium it is red (ruby), and when the impurity is a combination of the oxides of iron and titanium the colour is blue (sapphire). When the colour is caused by a trace of an accidental impurity the mineral is termed *allochromatic*. When the pigmenting material is an essential constituent of the mineral it is termed *idiochromatic*. The colour nuances exhibited by the various gemstones do provide a degree of assistance in their recognition to the experienced expert, but colour can never be an absolute guide as to the species of a stone and reliance can only be placed on accurate determination by the use of instruments.

It will be recalled that in the lesson on "Light" it was stated that when white (mixed) light passes through a coloured medium certain wave-lengths (colours) may be absorbed and the residual colours reaching the eye are blended together and produce the colour of the stone, *i.e.* selective absorption. Also it has been learnt that gems belonging to certain crystal systems split a ray of light into two rays. What happens then with such a stone—do both these rays undergo similar selective absorption, or do they differ one from another?

With doubly refractive stones there is often a difference in the selective absorption in the two rays, termed *differential selective absorption*, thus causing a difference in their colour. This effect is termed *dichroism* and is a valuable testing factor in gem testing. The effect of dichroism is rarely seen by the eye alone, hence, in order to observe these *twin colours*, as they are called, an instrument is necessary. This instrument is termed a *dichroscope*.

The dichroscope (fig. 38) consists of a short metal tube (A) closed at one end by a metal endplate (B), which has at its centre a square aperture (C). Into this tube slides another metal tube (D) which contains a rhomb of calcite (E), to the ends of which are cemented glass prisms (FF). The calcite rhomb is held securely in the tube by cork packing (GG) and at the end of

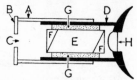

FIG. 38.—The parts of the dichroscope.

the tube is fitted a low power lens (H). The instrument may be focused by sliding the inner tube in or out, and some instruments have a special holder upon which the stone is fixed by wax to enable it to be more easily rotated.

On looking through the dichroscope at a light two images of the square aperture (C) are seen side by side, due to the strong double refraction of the calcite. To test a stone we place it close to the aperture, either on the stone holder or held by corn-tongs, and view it through the instrument held up to the light. If the two squares show identically the same colour the stone is *monochroic* and most probably singly refractive, but, if the two squares show a different colour, or even two different shades of the same colour, the stone is *dichroic* and MUST be doubly refractive.

Dichroism is due to double refraction, and therefore can never be seen in a singly refractive stone. It cannot, for obvious reasons, be observed with colourless or white stones even if they are doubly refracting, the dichroscope is only useful for coloured gems. Dichroism may be so feeble that it cannot be observed even by the dichroscope, and it is essential to remember that if a doubly refracting stone is examined by the instrument along the direction of an optic axis, no dichroism is seen even in a strongly dichroic stone. This is because the optic axis is a direction of single refraction in a doubly refractive stone.

Also dichroism cannot be seen when the vibration directions of the stone and the calcite rhomb of the dichroscope are at 45° to one another. The stone must be rotated and viewed through several different directions. The slightest difference in the colour of the two squares (or shade of the same colour) marks the stone as doubly refracting; it is not the exact colours that form the test but the fact that this difference in colour does or does not exist. The presence of "twin colours" is a sure sign that the stone is doubly refracting, but absence of dichroism does not necessarily mean that the stone is singly refracting.

The dichroscope will readily distinguish:

EMERALD from paste, soudé emerald (a composite stone) and "jewellers' olivine" (green garnet).

RUBY from paste, red spinel, "cape ruby" (garnet).

SAPPHIRE from paste, or blue spinel.

The dichroscope will not differentiate between the natural stones and their *synthetic* counterparts, for these latter gems have the same characters as the natural stones.

It has been explained that when a ray of white light is passed through a prism of glass, or for that matter, any other transparent medium, the ray will be *dispersed* into the familiar rainbow colours—red, through orange, yellow, green, blue, to violet. When Sir Isaac Newton in the year 1666 observed this effect, and thus showed that white light is composite, he paved the way for the *spectroscope*, one of the most powerful weapons known to present-day physical science.

Newton's first experiment consisted of passing a beam of sunlight, from a circular aperture in a shutter, through a glass prism and receiving the resulting colour band on a suitably placed screen. The aperture was of necessity rather wide and the colours of the resulting spectrum tended to overlap one another. That is, the spectrum was not *pure*. In 1802 Wollaston improved on the experiment by employing a ray of light which has passed through a narrow slit, which functions as a point of light in one dimension. Later, an optician of

Munich named Fraunhofer obtained a better spectrum on the screen by placing a convex lens between the slit and the prism, and for viewing the spectrum directly a telescope was fitted between the prism and the eye. Fraunhofer also experimented with a *grating* in place of the prism, thus following up the enunciation by Thomas Young in 1801, of the principle of interference.

Such arrangements of prisms, or grating, and lenses produce an instrument called a *spectroscope*, and by its aid various types of *spectra* can be observed. An ordinary gaslight or tungsten electric light will give a *continuous spectrum* with colours gradually changing from red at one end to violet at the other. The sun's spectrum is similar, but here the colours are crossed by fine dark lines called the *Fraunhofer lines*. A *bright line spectrum* is produced by the glowing vapours of elements and this is the type of spectrum used in *spectrum analysis*, for most elements give bright lines at fixed wave-lengths. A *fluorescence spectrum* may also consist of bright lines or bands, and, as will be seen later, such a spectrum has some importance in gemmology. The so-called *Swan spectrum* which has a fluted or banded formation relates to vapours of compounds and has no importance in this study. The type of spectra which interests gemmologists most is the *absorption spectra*.

The fundamental colour of a gemstone, as has been mentioned previously, depends upon which wave-lengths (colours) are absorbed from the incident white light. The residual colours, *i.e.* those not absorbed, pass through the stone and combine to produce the colour of the stone. Hence if light which has passed through a stone is examined by a spectroscope, it will be seen that those parts of the spectrum totally absorbed appear as dark spaces, and those partially absorbed as areas of low intensity. Careful examination will show that many stones have sharp dark (sometimes bright) lines crossing the bright parts of the spectrum which often afford valuable additional evidence as to the nature of a stone.

These absorption spectra were first considered in relation to gemstones through the publication, by A. H. Church in 1866, of notes on the narrow dark bands seen in the spectrum produced when white light has passed through a zircon. In recent years E. T. Wherry in America and B. W. Anderson with C. J. Payne in this country have carried out research and published data of the absorption bands found in many of the gem materials. These absorption bands are in general due to some chemical compound or compounds which are an impurity in the stone and which may, or may not, be the cause of the stone's colour.

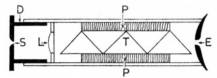

FIG. 39.—Diagram showing the parts of a direct-vision prism spectroscope.

As to a choice of instrument best suited for the examination of the absorption spectra of gemstones the most useful seems to be the direct-vision hand instruments which have a fairly high dispersion. Whether the instrument is one of the prism type, or the type which functions by the principle of interference by the use of a diffraction grating, is of little consequence. It should be noted, however, that the grating instrument produces a spectrum in which the dispersion is uniform throughout the scale, whereas the spectrum produced by the prism instrument is found to be bunched-up at the red end and has a much wider dispersion at the violet end. A detail which should be mentioned is that the instrument should preferably be provided with an adjustable slit. The instruments found most suitable in general practice are the direct-vision instruments with adjustable slit. Fig. 39 shows the parts of a direct-vision prism spectroscope. There are two usual methods of observation with the spectroscope—by transmitted light and by scattered light. The best technique for transmitted light is to use the spectroscope in conjunction with a microscope. The specimen to be tested is placed, table facet down, on a microscope slide placed on the stage of a microscope and illuminated by a strong source of light *via* the mirror and the substage condenser. Using a low power objective (1 in. or 1½ in.), the eyepiece is removed and the microscope focused until the whole field of view in the body tube is filled with bright light which has passed through the specimen. The spectroscope is now set by adjusting both the focus and the width of the slit. This may conveniently be done by holding the instrument towards a source of light which has a "line" structure and making such adjustments to ensure that the lines are a suitable width and are sharply focused. Suitable "line" illumination may be a sodium discharge lamp; the Fraunhofer lines of the sun's spectrum, or the underlying emission lines—bright lines—of the mercury vapour as seen in an electric fluorescent tube lamp. This light is viewed with the spectroscope, which is held in place of the microscope eyepiece. To examine by scattered light the stone is placed on a piece of black cloth and illuminated by a strong light; the microscope stand condenser is useful to converge the light on to the specimen, and the spectroscope held in the hand and directed on to the stone, the instrument thus analysing the light that is reflected and scattered from the stone. This method appears to be the better practice when it is required to observe the bright fluorescence lines and the first explained method for general work.

The acuity of the eye is less for the violet end of the spectrum than it is for the red, so that if the red part of the spectrum is obliterated in some way the absorption bands in the blue part of the spectrum may be more easily seen. This may be accomplished by using before the strong light used to illuminate the specimen a flask filled with a solution of copper sulphate. Such a solution passes blue and violet light but absorbs the red, yellow and most of the green, thus cutting out the over readily visible rays of longer wave-length.

Those stones which show pronounced absorption bands and thus assist in their identification are listed below:

ZIRCON usually shows many sharp dark lines crossing an otherwise clear spectrum. The strongest and most prominent are at 6600A, 6535A, 5890A. (Table appended below this list shows where these measurements are in the colour band.) The "fired" white and blue zircons may show only the line at 6535A and then only faintly. These absorption bands are due to a trace of compounds of uranium.

RUBY shows absorption bands due to an oxide of the metal chromium, to which compound is also due the colour of the stone. This spectrum then shows a broad absorption in the yellow and green and in the indigo and violet. This leaves a "window" in the blue in which may be seen two sharp lines at 4750A and 4680A. The line at 4750A is seen with an instrument of large dispersion to be two lines very close together; this is termed a *doublet*. Examination of the red and orange end of the spectrum shows several dark lines, such as one at 6590A and one at 6935A, which, instead of being dark, is generally seen as bright red (due to a fluorescence effect) and under high dispersion this bright red line is seen to be a close doublet.

EMERALD, which is also coloured by chromium, shows in general a similar type of spectrum to that of ruby except that the broad absorption is not so pronounced. There are no strong lines in the blue. The lines in the red are all sharp and are dark. The most prominent bands are at 6830A, 6805A, 6620A, 6460A and 6295A.

ALEXANDRITE shows bands due to chromium and somewhat similar to emerald. The important lines are at 6795A, 6510A and 6450A.

RED SPINEL is also coloured by chromium and shows a typical chromium spectrum without the lines in the blue "window." It shows a dark band at 6560A and a "band" made up of four or five lines close together which are often bright red (fluorescent lines).

BLUE SPINEL shows a band in the orange at 6300A of moderate strength, a somewhat stronger and narrower band at 4800A and a strong broad band at 4590A. This spectrum is due to ferrous iron.

DEMANTOID GARNET is most certainly coloured by chromium, but owing to the general absorption in the red it is difficult to find lines so characteristic of that metal. At 4420A there is an absorption band due to iron which, owing to the general absorption of the violet, may appear as a sharp cut-off when no violet is seen beyond the band.

PERIDOT shows a spectrum due to iron compounds which are actual ingredients of the stone and not an impurity. Three bands are seen which are rather broad and are centred at 4970A, 4730A and 4530A.

BLUE SAPPHIRE shows a band, generally rather sharp, at 4500A. This band may not always be seen (*see note under synthetic blue sapphire*).

GREEN SAPPHIRE shows the band at 4500A as seen in the blue sapphire, only much stronger and with other bands at 4710 and 4600. Both in blue and green sapphire the band is due to iron compounds.

ORANGE-YELLOW SAPPHIRE shows the iron band at 4500A as for the blue and green sapphires. This band is seen particularly strongly in the blue, green and orange sapphires from Australia, but the Ceylon yellow sapphires do not exhibit any bands.

YELLOW CHRYSOBERYL shows an iron band at 4440A.

ALMANDINE GARNET shows several broad bands, the most easily seen being the three centred at (*a*) 5740A, (*b*) 5260A and (*c*) 5040A. In dark specimens (*b*) and (*c*) may look like one broad band.

PYROPE GARNET in general contains some percentage of almandine in its constitution, and hence shows the almandine bands although somewhat less strongly. If the stone approximates to nearly pure pyrope, that is to R.I. $= 1·74$ and S.G. $= 3·68$, the spectrum is reminiscent of that for red spinel. The lines in red are not so easily discerned and there are *never* any fluorescent lines.

PINK and GREEN TOURMALINES do not as a rule show a distinctive spectrum. The band at 4980A sometimes present in green tourmalines is too weak to be decisive. The only colour of tourmaline which shows anything like a good spectrum is the violet-red "siberite" variety which shows several bands.

YELLOW APATITE can usually be identified by the group of fine lines in the yellow and a smaller and less prominent group in the green of the spectrum. These are the lines of the rare earth didymium. These very characteristic lines are seen, but usually very weakly, in all calcium minerals.

SYNTHETIC GEMS

Synthetic ruby shows a similar spectrum to that of the natural ruby.

Synthetic blue, green and orange sapphires *never* show the iron band at 4500A. (*If a suspected stone is found to show this band in the blue-violet the stone must be natural. Absence of the band does not necessarily prove that the stone is synthetic, for some natural blue sapphires have been found which do not show the band, or show it too weakly for it to be easily seen.*) Blue synthetic spinels show a spectrum due to cobalt; these stones usually imitate the blue zircon and the blue aquamarine. The spectrum consists of three broad bands centred at 6350A, 5800A and 5400A. The yellow synthetic spinel shows a spectrum having two bands in the blue-violet at 4450A and 4220A. This spectrum is probably due to manganese and may be found in combination with the cobalt spectrum mentioned previously. The "Alexandrite" types of synthetic corundum and spinel do not show the bands in the red as are found in the natural Alexandrite chrysoberyl. The "Alexandrite colour" synthetic sapphire shows a fine line in the blue at 4750A, while the "Alexandrite colour" synthetic spinel shows the three cobalt bands. These bands of cobalt are prominent in many blue pastes, but in glass these bands are separated further apart. Red pastes usually show a broad band in the yellow.

As a guide to where the wave-lengths given in Angstrom unit come in the spectrum the following table is appended:

TABLE OF APPROXIMATE WAVE-LENGTHS

7000A to 6500A	...	...	... RED.
6500A to 6000A	...	...	... ORANGE.
6000A to 5500A	...	...	... YELLOW.
5500A to 5000A	...	...	... GREEN.
5000A to 4500A	...	...	... BLUE.
4500A to 4000A	...	...	... VIOLET.

It has long been known that when an emerald is viewed through certain colour filters which transmit a band of red and a band of green light the stone appears red. This is due to the fact that emerald passes a considerable amount of red light. These filters have been made in various forms, but only one type appears to have received much favour. This is the type known as the Chelsea Colour Filter, which consists of two gelatine filters between glass or plastic plates and may be obtained from the Secretary of the Gemmological Association, Saint Dunstan's House, Carey Lane, London, E.C.2. The filter, as before mentioned, shows emerald as red and its glass and doublet (composite stones, as soudé emerald) counterfeits as green, thus giving a clear distinction between the two. It must be mentioned that all other green gemstones also show green through the filter, with the exception of green zircons, demantoid garnets and the stained chalcedony coloured by chromium compounds. The filter also differentiates between the synthetic blue spinels from the blue zircon and aquamarine which they simulate. The spinels show orange or red through the filter, while the natural stones show greenish. Rubies and red spinels appear to glow with their own light (fluorescence effect) when viewed through the filter, while garnets appear dull and lifeless.

LUMINESCENCE AND ELECTRICAL EFFECTS

LUMINESCENCE may be expressed as the glow of visible light observed in a number of substances under certain conditions; the light being *cold* for the substance is not in the state of incandescence. Science knows different types of luminescence and these are given names which are derived from the initiating cause. Thus there are: *chemiluminescence*, as exemplified by the glow shown by slowly oxidising phosphorus; *bioluminescence*, which is a form of chemiluminescence, and is shown by the glows of fire-flies and glow-worms and by decaying flesh. *Triboluminescence*, when the glow is produced by scratching or rubbing, *e.g.* some zinc blende, and *thermoluminescence*, developed by low heating, and really a pre-charged luminescence or long delayed afterglow resuscitated by the heat, have little place in gem study. *Electroluminescence*, induced by a passage of current, is shown by blue diamonds when a test is made for electroconductivity. The type of luminescence which interests the student of gemmology is that termed *photoluminescence*, when the glow is induced by visible and ultra-violet light. X-rays and cathode rays produce similar effects. Most important in our study is the luminescence produced when a substance is irradiated with ultra-violet light.

What is luminescence? It was shown by Stokes, using a "crossed filter" technique, that the emitted radiation, the visible glow of light, is of longer wave-length than that of the exciting radiation inducing the glow. The substance therefore "transforms" the radiation. Further, the term *fluorescence* is used for the light emitted when the incident rays are impinging on the substance, and *phosphorescence* for the "afterglow" or continuation of light, if present, after the exciting rays are cut off. Solid substances which luminesce are called *phosphors*. There are two types: *intrinsic phosphors* which are pure substances— and the only one which interests us is diamond where the luminescence is probably due to lattice defects in the crystal structure; the other type is the *impurity activated phosphor* where impurities, called *activators*, produce luminescent centres.

Briefly, luminescence is the absorption of radiant energy by the substance. This raises an electron from a stable orbit (the so-called *ground state*) to a higher energy level (the so-called *excited state*), from which it immediately returns, giving up its energy in the form of some sort of light emission. This is fluorescence. If, as in some cases, the excited electron does not immediately return to ground state but becomes trapped in a metastable level it cannot return to ground state. It is then necessary for the electron to receive further energy in order to bring it back to the excited state from which it can return to ground state with the emission of light. Thus there is a delay in producing an "after-glow" or phosphorescence.

Ultra-violet light is made up of those radiations of shorter wavelengths than those of visible light, say below 4000A, and go down to about 150A. There are, however, physical reasons why wave-lengths below about 2000A cannot be utilized. The useful range is therefore from 4000A to 2000A. These radiations are conveniently divided into two sections; those between 4000A and 3000A which are termed the long-wave ultra-violet range, and between 3000A and 2000A, termed the short-wave range. The importance of the two divisions lies in the fact that the response of a given material may differ considerably when different ranges of ultra-violet light impinge upon them and this differential luminescence may be of diagnostic value.

There are many sources of ultra-violet light, including the sun, arc-lamps, etc., but the most efficient type of generator for analysis work is some form of mercury-vapour lamp in conjunction with special glass filters. There are three types of mercury-vapour lamps used in gem testing. They are, first, the medium-pressure mercury-vapour lamp which gives out an intense visible light of bluish colour, a strong emission at 3650A (long-wave ultra-violet) and also a strong emission at 2537A in the short-wave region. This lamp used in conjunction with a Wood's glass filter which cuts out most of the visible light and also the 2537A band but allows to pass the 3650A provides the most efficient and powerful long-wave ultra-violet lamp.

To isolate the 2537A line all that one might consider to be needed would be a filter cutting out the visible and the 3650A band from the medium pressure lamp just described. No filter yet made will do this and the only way to get a 2537A emission is by way of compromise. To do this a low-pressure mercury discharge lamp has an envelope made of a glass which will pass the 2537A line. Such a low-pressure lamp emits strongly the 2537A line; much less of the 3560A and visible emissions, and when used in conjunction with a special filter (Chance OX7 filter is one) the unwanted rays are to a great extent suppressed and only the short-wave ultra-violet rays come through strongly. This is the standard short-wave lamp.

The third lamp is a hybrid for it is essentially a short-wave lamp as above. The difference lies in the fact that the glass envelope does not pass the short-wave radiation (2537A) and, further, the inside of the tube is coated with a "fluorescent" coating, which under the influence of short-wave ultra-violet rays, "fluoresces" with long-wave ultra-violet light. A special filter helps to suppress the feeble visible light from such a lamp, which differs from the medium-pressure long-wave ultra-violet lamp in that the emission is continuous from about 4100A in the visible to about 3200A in the ultra-violet.

THE LUMINESCENT GLOWS SHOWN BY GEMSTONES

Unless otherwise stated the effects are as seen under long-wave ultra-violet light.

Diamond.

"*Cape series*" (colourless and yellow stones) glow blue to deep violet.

"*Brown series*" (brown and green stones) glow with a green light.

Certain colourless, brown and green stones glow with a yellow fluorescence (strongly blue fluorescing diamonds show a yellow phosphorescence).

Pink diamonds sometimes glow with an orange light.

Natural blue diamonds do not as a rule glow sufficiently strongly to overcome the residual light from the lamp, but after short-wave ultra-violet radiation such stones are seen to phosphoresce with a yellow light.

Corundum.

Ruby (natural and synthetic). A crimson glow with all wavebands which is due to the chromium ion. The stones show a discrete fluorescence spectrum. *Violet and pink sapphires* behave like ruby. *Synthetic rubies* generally show a crimson phosphorescence under X-ray irradiation.

Natural blue sapphires are inert, for the iron they contain inhibits the luminescence, but the *synthetic blue sapphires* glow with a green light under the short-wave ultra-violet lamp.

Natural green sapphires are inert but the *synthetic green sapphires* glow with an orange light.

Yellow sapphires are variable; the stones from Ceylon show an apricot-coloured glow, but the more greenish-yellow stones from Siam and Australia do not luminesce. *Synthetic yellow* sapphires show a weak crimson glow.

The *colourless natural sapphire* usually shows a weak orange glow, while the *synthetic white sapphire* is usually inert, but cases have been noted where a whitish glow is seen under the short-wave ultra-violet lamp.

Beryl.

The *natural emeralds* usually show a green glow but in some cases a red glow is seen.

The *synthetic emeralds* usually show a strong crimson, or, as in the French synthetic emerald, an orange glow. For emeralds the "fluorescent tube" lamp is probably best, but it is well to try all radiations when attempting to separate synthetic and natural emeralds, and to use control stones for direct comparison.

Aquamarines and the fancy beryls are generally inert. The so-called "synthetic aquamarines" are really synthetic spinels and these do glow under ultra-violet light. They are mentioned later.

Garnet.

All garnets seem to be inert, except the massive grossular garnet from the Transvaal which shows an orange glow under X-rays. This effect may be used to differentiate the so-called "Transvaal jade" from the true jades which do not glow.

Zircon.

The mustard coloured glow shown by most *zircons* is fairly characteristic, but the effect is very variable and often masked by the colour of the stone. It is unwise to examine the heat-treated colourless and blue zircons under the lamp as it has the effect of reverting the stones to their original brownish colour. The synthetic spinels which are so-called "synthetic blue zircon" behave differently and will be mentioned under spinel.

Topaz.

The yellow *precious topaz* from Brazil glows with a yellowish hue, but other colours of topaz may show yellowish, bluish or whitish glows.

Spinel.

Both *red and pink, natural and synthetic, spinels* show a crimson glow, like that of ruby, and like ruby the glow is due to the chromium ion. The stones show a discrete fluorescence spectrum, which, however, differs from that of ruby. This will be referred to later when the "crossed filter" technique is mentioned. Owing to their iron content *natural dark blue spinels* are inert, but the pale blue and violet stones show various green or red glows. *Synthetic white spinels* are inert under the long-wave ultra-violet lamp but show a bluish white glow under the short-wave ultra-violet lamp. The *synthetic blue spinels* which are made to imitate the blue sapphire, aquamarine and zircon show red under the long-wave ultra-violet lamp and whitish under the short-wave ultra-violet lamp, and so does the *synthetic dark green ("tourmaline colour") spinel*. The light greens and yellow colours in synthetic spinels show a bright apple green luminescence under all radiations. This is said to be due to manganese.

Other stones.

   Fluorspar generally glows blue or violet, but the Blue John variety is inert. *Kunzite* glows orange. *Benitoite* glows blue under the short-wave ultra-violet lamp only being inert under the long-wave lamp. This gives a distinction from natural sapphire. *Scheelite* is another stone which fluoresces a blue colour under the short-wave lamp, but does not luminesce under long-wave radiations.

   Stokes used a "crossed filter" technique to prove his assertion that fluorescence is a change of wave-length; Anderson applied the method to gem testing. Briefly, the method involves placing before a strong white light a filter, usually a flask containing a saturated solution of copper sulphate, which passes blue and violet light but absorbs the red, orange, yellow and most of the green; and holding before the eye a filter which passes only red light. This is usually a glass or gelatine filter. The patch of blue light seen, projected on to a black cloth provided before the lamp and filter, is obliterated when the red filter is placed before the eye. On setting any red-fluorescing stone/s, such as ruby, spinel or emerald, on the patch of blue light illuminating the black cloth, and viewing the stone through the red filter, the stones are seen brilliantly red—like glowing coals. A practical elaboration is to use a spectroscope in place of the red filter. Then the rubies will show the typical sharp bright red line with a broader (two-line) band nearer the orange. On the other hand the natural red spinels will show a typical close group of five bright lines, two being stronger than the others—in fact the so-called "organ-pipe" fluorescent line structure. It must be noted, however, that the synthetic red spinels show a ruby type fluorescence spectrum.

At this stage something may be said about those very short-wave invisible radiations discovered by Röntgen in 1895 which are popularly called X-rays. These rays have a mean wave-length of 1 Angstrom unit. There are three methods whereby these rays may be used in gem-testing; first by the power they have of penetrating different substances in different degrees. This generally depends upon the atomic weight of the elements present, thus, diamond with the low atomic weight of carbon is very transparent to the rays, while zircon with its heavy element zirconium is comparatively opaque. Secondly a narrow beam of X-rays may be reflected from planes of atoms in a crystal. Such a narrow beam of X-rays allowed to pass along a symmetry axis of a crystal will produce on a suitably placed photographic film a pattern of spots indicative of the symmetry axis traversed. This method is used in some forms of pearl testing and will be referred to again when pearls are discussed. X-rays can, like ultraviolet rays, induce a visible glow of light in some substances and observation of these X-ray fluorescences and phosphorescences is often of diagnostic value.

X-rays are produced when electrons moving at high speeds are suddenly stopped by striking a solid body, such as the target of an X-ray tube. The characteristics of the X-ray beam depends upon a number of factors which include the degree of vacuum of the tube, the speed of the electrons (controlled by the voltage across the tube), and the quantity of the electrons which is dependant upon the temperature of the filament which is controlled by the current supplied to it and measured in milliamperes. In the schematic diagram of an X-ray tube (fig. 40), B is the evacuated bulb, A the anode or target, F the filament, S.S. are "shields" with negative bias to focus the electrons on to the target, and E is the electron stream.

At the other end of the visible spectrum lie the infra-red rays, but

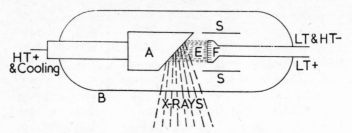

FIG. 40.—Schematic diagram of an X-ray tube.

owing to technical difficulties very little work has been carried out with them on gem materials.

There are various electrical effects which occur in crystals, and gem crystals particularly, but mostly these have an interest solely for the scientist or for the electronics engineer. They need no further discussion here. There are two electrical effects which may with advantage be mentioned. They are, firstly, the so-called *pyroelectric*

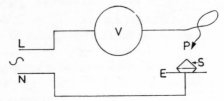

FIG. 41.—A simple circuit for testing a stone for electro-conductivity.

effect where an electric charge of different sign is developed at opposite ends of an axis of symmetry. This occurs in tourmaline and is the probable cause of such stones collecting dust when in a heated shop window. The second is the fact that certain stones will conduct electricity when inserted into a suitable electrical circuit. Although some work has been carried out on these effects in gem stones it is only in the case of blue diamond that this *electroconductivity* is used as a test. All natural blue diamonds have been found to conduct electricity, whereas those blue diamonds which owe their blue colour to atomic bombardment do *not* conduct electricity. Fig. 41 shows a suitable circuit for such an apparatus to detect this electroconductivity; L is the line side of the alternating current of the mains circuit and N the neutral side (batteries may be used in place of the mains); V is a suitable voltmeter, E the electrode upon which the stone to be tested is rested, and P is the probe to make contact with the stone.

Anderson has carried out experiments on the magnetism of gem materials as an aid to testing. The necessary procedures are somewhat complicated and any interested worker should consult larger reference works.

THE MICROSCOPE

THE last instrument to be discussed is the microscope, which, in the simpler types, is simply a convenient carrier for a compound system of lenses, means for the adjustment of their focus and for control of the illumination of the specimen under examination. The primary function of the microscope is to give an enlarged image of an object set at its focus. The instrument performs in a much better manner, and with a much greater magnifying power, the duty of a simple hand magnifier (or loupe) which is indeed itself a simple type of microscope.

The instrument (fig. 42) consists of a *foot*, to which is attached by trunnions, so that the instrument may be used vertically or in an inclined position, the *limb* complete with *body tube* and its rackwork for focusing. The *eyepiece* and *objective* are mounted at either end of the body tube, which is of such length that these two lens systems correctly amplify one another. The focusing adjustments are two in number, a *coarse adjustment* by spiral rack and pinion, and a *fine adjustment* controlled by a finely-threaded screw system.

Below the body tube, and fixed to the limb, is the *stage*, which is a metal plate (or platform) with its plane at right angles to the length of the body tube. This platform, upon which is placed the object to be examined, has an aperture at its centre (that is in the optical axis of the instrument) and is usually provided with spring clips to hold the plain glass specimen slips. Below the stage is a continuation of the limb which carries an arm to which is fixed, in a gimbal device, a mirror for directing a beam of light through the aperture of the stage, through the specimen under examination and up through the objective, body tube and eyepiece. This mirror is a double one, one

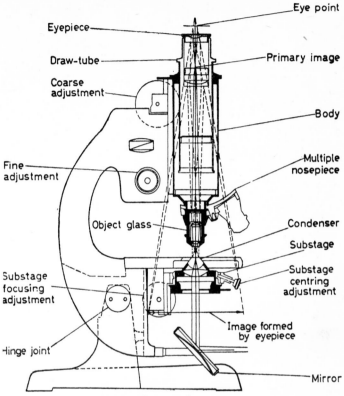

FIG. 42.—The parts of a microscope.

side being plane and the other slightly concave; the former is to be used in daylight and the latter with artificial light so as to obtain as nearly as possible parallelization of the beam of light passing up and into the instrument.

The magnifying power of a microscope is altered by the use of objectives of different focal length and can be altered also with a change of eyepiece. For gem-testing work an objective of a $\frac{2}{3}$-in. focal length is the most powerful which can be employed; it will be found, however, that powers of 1 in. and 1½ in. are the most suitable for all general work, for the focal length is wide enough comfortably to clear the stone with the addition of a bright and wide field of view. Should the stone under test be set, say in a ring, and it is necessary to observe the stone when it is immersed in a liquid (see later), the shank of the ring is found to stick upward and hence prevent the objective being lowered sufficiently to "get into the stone," a 1½-in. objective will be found to give sufficient clearance in such a case. A useful accessory for a microscope is a substage condenser, consisting of a "bee-hive" lens system and completed with an *iris* diaphragm, the whole being arranged to allow for movement up and down and also for the whole condenser to be swung clear of the optical axis of the microscope.

The use for such a microscope as has just been described is primarily for the examination of the surface and internal structure of gems, as in the case of suspected synthetic stones. This simple type of microscope is also suitable to carry out the Becke test described in the chapter "Refractive Index Measurement." To use a microscope the instrument should be placed before a window or a table lamp on a firm table with the tube in a vertical position. The mirror should be adjusted so that the maximum amount of light enters the lower lens system, *i.e.* the objective which should be the one with the power it is required to use. On looking down the eyepiece the field of view should be seen to be quite bright. If a gemstone is now placed on a glass slip resting (or clipped) on the stage it will be seen that even when the microscope is carefully focused with the coarse adjustment (the fine adjustment is rarely necessary with any objective over ½ in. in focal length) the inside of the stone can hardly be seen. This is due to reflections from the surface of the stone; hence it is necessary to use another technique to enable the internal structure to be seen. To a certain extent these surface reflections may be overcome by the use of the substage condenser; the best method, however, is to view the stone when it is immersed in a vessel of glass filled with highly refractive oil. This oil or liquid should have nearly the same index of refraction as the stone being examined, and the two most commonly used are methylene iodide and monobromonaphthalene. To avoid damage to the soft glass of the objective lens care should be taken not to rack the tube down on to the stone. If the microscope is first lowered nearly on to the cell of liquid and stone while looking sideways to ensure that the objective does not come in contact with the surface of the liquid, the observation can then be made by raising the tube and thus bringing the bottom edge of the stone into focus first. Further slow racking up will enable the observer to view the inside of the stone from bottom to top, that is, the stone will have been "worked through" without any danger of the microscope being racked down on to the stone with the consequent damage to the objective or to the cell.

So far the discussion has centred around the simple microscope; most microscopes used for gem-testing purposes are fitted with an arrangement to produce plane polarized light in order that specimens may be viewed with such light. The best types, and incidentally very expensive, of these microscopes are the *petrological microscopes* (fig. 43) used by mineralogists and geologists in the study of rocks. They are fitted with a stage which is capable of rotation and graduated in degrees. They are supplied with an *analyzer* and *polarizer*, which are special prisms of calcite termed Nicol's prism or discs of Polaroid, and the fine adjustment is graduated to read 1/100 millimetres—that is the amount the tube has been raised or lowered by altering the fine adjustment can be determined from the difference in the readings of the first position and the second. This is particularly useful when it is necessary to determine the refractive index by the direct measurement method described in the instalment on refractive index measurement. The best petrological microscopes have other accessories, which have little use in general testing and will be ignored for the purpose of these notes.

One point that cannot be ignored is the use of polarized light in the testing of gemstones. As before mentioned, ordinary light vibrates in all directions perpendicular to the path of the ray, while polarized

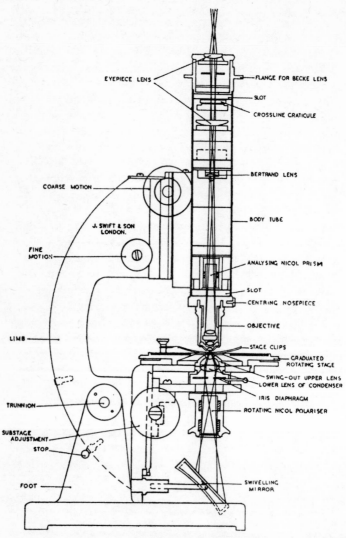

FIG. 43.—The parts of a petrological microscope.

light has only one direction of vibration perpendicular to the path of the ray. In doubly refracting crystals (remember crystals of all systems other than the cubic are doubly refracting) the two rays are plane polarized in directions at right angles to one another. Now if plane polarized light can be produced which is vibrating in the direction, say, east/west (in the plane of the paper) and above it, plane polarized light can be produced vibrating north/south, the ray from the first polarizer will be unable to get through the second polarizer, or as it is termed, the *analyzer*. This position of two polarizing pieces is termed the *crossed position*. If between these two polarizers is placed a doubly refracting stone which has the two rays of its double refraction vibrating in the east/west and north/south positions, it will be obvious that the stone will have imposed no new vibration-directions on the rays, and thus the "crossed" effect of polarizer and analyzer is still maintained and no light is transmitted. On rotating the stone, however, the vibration-directions are no longer dead against either nicol and a certain amount of light passes. The maximum light is seen at 45° to the "extinction" position. If an apparatus is arranged whereby a polarizer and an analyzer are respectively below and above a rotating stage (to carry the stone), assuming the polarizers to be in the crossed position and a doubly refracting stone between them, a rotation of the stage with the stone will give a field which is four times light and four times dark. This is a proof of double refraction. Singly refractive materials such as glass and cubic minerals give a dark field during the complete rotation.

There are several methods whereby the observation of double refraction by the use of polarized light may be carried out. However, with the exception of a short note at the end, these notes will be confined to the use of Nicol's prisms, or POLAROID discs, in conjunction with a microscope. The next consideration is, "What is a Nicol's prism and how does it work?" (these prisms are often called "nicols" for short). The prism consists of two pieces of calcite (Iceland Spar) cemented together by Canada Balsam (R.I. = 1·54) in such a manner that the ordinary ray, having a higher index of refraction than the balsam, is totally reflected at the balsam surface and is absorbed by the casing of the prism. On the other hand, the extraordinary ray, which has a lower refractive index than the balsam, emerges as a completely polarized ray of light at the other end of the prism (see fig. 44). One of these prisms is mounted in a holder below the stage.

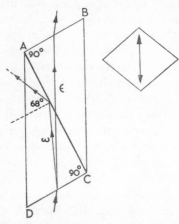

FIG. 44.—Nicol prism showing absorption of the totally reflected ordinary ray and the direct passage through of the extraordinary ray. A, B, C, D = calcite prism. A, C = canada balsam cement layer. Small drawing shows direction of vibration of the emergent ray through the top end of the nicol prism.

This fitting allows this lower nicol or the *polarizer*, as it is termed, to be rotated. The second nicol or *analyzer* is placed in the tube of the microscope above the objective, or above the eyepiece.

In order to use the microscope for the detection of double refraction the instrument is set up as for ordinary observation and the nicols are placed in the optical axis of the instrument. In the best instruments the analyzer is constructed so that it can be pushed in or out of the tube; in others the analyzer has to be screwed on to the tube in place of the objective, which is then screwed into the bottom of the nicol. In view of the increased use of POLAROID discs in place of nicol prisms the term "polars" is used in place of "nicols." Most types allow the lower nicol to be swung out of the optical axis, in a similar manner to the condensing lens. With the nicols in position they are *crossed* by rotating the lower prism until no light is seen through the microscope eyepiece (the better instruments have a click which sets the lower nicol in the crossed position). The stone to be examined is now placed in a cell of highly refractive liquid, the whole placed on the stage and focused. The rotating stage is then slowly turned through a complete circle.

If the field remains dark the stone must be singly refracting, but if alternately light and dark four times during a complete revolution the stone must be doubly refracting and hence belong to either the hexagonal, trigonal, tetragonal, rhombic, monoclinic or triclinic crystal system. Some glasses and some stones of the cubic system may be found that will show light through a different position during a complete rotation; this is due to strain and

FIG. 45. — The Rutland polariscope.

is termed *anomalous double refraction.* Careful observation shows that this patchy brightness never takes place sharply at every quarter revolution.

Certain materials, particularly those under some form of strain, show an irregular patchy "field" of light and dark areas. This "anomalous double refraction" is commonly seen in synthetic spinels, many garnets and some pastes, but in all these cases the extinction of light sharply four times during a complete circle of revolution is rarely seen.

It is not absolutely necessary to have a polarizing apparatus fitted into a microscope and a number of makes of small polarizing instruments of pocket or near pocket size are marketed. These use POLAROID discs and a most convenient one of these small polarizers is the Rutland polariscope (fig. 45).

The main use of the microscope is to examine the inclusions in gemstones in order to determine whether the stone is of natural origin, a synthetic production or a glass. The inclusions seen in gemstones may be divided into types: *pre-existing* inclusions are those present before the formation of the host crystal, and such inclusions are usually seen to be solid crystals or "earthy" matter; the second, called the *contemporary* inclusions, consist of features which have formed at the same time as the host crystal. They may be drops of mother liquid or crystals which have grown at the same time. The third type are inclusions which have formed later than the host crystal, and include such features as the so-called *healing feathers*, which are cracks in which the mineral-rich liquid included in the cracks has crystallized out, or by alteration a type of inclusion called ex-solution occurs by chemical action. Some inclusions are so typical of a gemstone that they may be used to identify them, or they may indicate the country of origin of the stone. Examples of these are the asbestos fibres in "horse-tail" arrangement which characterizes the green demantoid garnet and the curved growth lines of the synthetic corundums. The three-phase inclusions, which are cavities containing a liquid, a bubble of gas and a cubic crystal, are evidence that the stone is an emerald from the Colombian mines. Round clear "bubble-like" crystals and fine crossed needles, called "silk," of the ruby from Burma show a difference from the dark crystal surrounded by a circular feather which is the characteristic picture of Siam rubies. The curved colour bands so indicative of the synthetic corundums are not seen in the synthetic spinels, but in both cases the included bubbles are of typical types and may be round, tadpole-shaped or flask-shaped. Bubbles in glass are nearly always round or elliptical in shape, and glass often shows swirls like stirred treacle. Synthetic emeralds, owing to their different method of growth, show natural-looking feathers, but the experienced eye can detect the difference in these features from those in natural emerald.

THE GEM SPECIES

HAVING dealt with the basic principles underlying the testing of gemstones, and gained an insight into the working of the instruments used for this purpose, it now seems clear that the next course must entail some discussion of the gem materials themselves. This lesson will, therefore, consist of a survey of the natural mineral species which have a major use in jewellery.

It will be seen that the method adopted in these notes is a tabular treatment giving only the essential data. Historical aspects, romance and superstition are ignored. For a full and more complete information on the species the reader is referred to one of the larger textbooks.

(The following abbreviations will be used throughout this tabulated list: H. = Hardness; S.G. = Specific gravity; R.I. = Refractive index.)

DIAMOND

Carbon (C); Cubic, common forms: octahedron (8 sides), dodecahedron (12 sides), trisoctahedron (24 sides), hexoctahedron (48 sides) and rarely cubes (6 sides). Faces are often distorted and curved, some crystals are almost spherical. "Spinel twin" crystals are common and flattened twins are termed "macles." The varieties are: (*a*) Gem variety; colourless and pale shades of pink, blue, yellow, green and brown. (*b*) Boart; minutely crystalline grey to black crystals useless as gems but powdered for use in cutting and polishing. Term also used for small off-coloured and flawed crystals used for the same purpose. (*c*) Carbon, carbonardo or black diamond; crypto-crystalline material composed of diamond, graphite and amorphous carbon generally used for industrial purposes.

$H. = 10$. Slight variation with direction, octahedral face the hardest and cube face the softest. Reported variation in hardness of crystals from different localities may be solely due to the existence of twinning. *Cleavage* = octahedral and perfect. $S.G. = 3\cdot52$ and is very constant through the purity of the crystals (the impure boart may be as low as $3\cdot15$). The lustre of diamond is adamantine and the refraction single. Sometimes anomalous double refraction may be observed which is due to strain. $R.I. = 2\cdot42$. The dispersion is very strong and is exceeded only by sphene, demantoid garnet, cassiterite and blende, and the synthetic stones rutile and strontium titanate. This property is, as readers will remember, responsible for the display of colour known as "fire" so well seen in diamond. Under ultra-violet light diamonds fluoresce, usually sky blue or violet, but yellow and brown fluorescence colours have been observed. Diamonds also phosphoresce; are transparent to X-rays, and yellow and colourless diamonds, after long and intimate contact with radium salts, assume a green or greenish-blue colour and attain a degree of radio-activity. Modernly the colour of diamonds is altered by bombarding them with high-speed atomic particles. This will be discussed in a later chapter.

Scientists have divided diamonds into groups, the most important being the Type I and Type II groups. Type I diamonds are the most commonly met in gem quality stones and are characterized by their absorption of the ultra-violet below about 3000A and by an absorption band in the infra-red. Type II diamonds are those which transmit ultra-violet to about 2250A, and this Type II group is divided into two sub-groups Type IIa and Type IIb, the latter being interesting as natural blue-coloured diamonds are of this Type IIb and these stones are electro-conducting.

The occurrence of diamond was known from historical times in India, and some mining from a "pipe" and alluvial deposits is now carried on. Diamond was discovered in Brazil in 1728, South Africa in 1867, Guyana in 1887, South-West Africa in 1908, Belgian Congo and Angola in 1910 and Ghana in 1919. Diamonds are also found in Russia (pipes and alluvial), Australia and Borneo.

With the exception of South Africa the diamonds are all found in gravels and conglomerates derived from basic igneous rocks. The name given to the gravel from which the diamonds are found in Brazil is *cascalho*. In South Africa there are two contrasted modes of occurrence: (*a*) River diggings; diamonds found in the river beds around the Vaal river and in alluvial material some several miles each side of the river. (*b*) "Dry" diggings or mines; consisting of vertical pipes cutting down through various beds of rock to an unknown depth. These pipes are filled with a rock called "peridotite," a bluish-coloured rock with a high iron content termed the "blue ground." Near the surface the "blue ground" weathers to a yellow colour and is then termed the "yellow ground." The surrounding rocks are described as "reef." Diamonds are found in the blue and yellow ground but never in the reef. The synthesis of diamond has been accomplished but the product consists of crystals too small to be used for anything except the production of diamond powder. Later syntheses have produced gem quality diamonds but they are relatively small and cost more to produce than the mined stones.

CORUNDUM

Oxide of aluminium (alumina) (Al_2O_3); Trigonal, ruby in six-sided prisms with basal plane and sapphire in 12-sided bi-pyramids. Sapphire crystals often barrel-shaped. Varieties: red (ruby), blue (sapphire), yellow, green, purple and colourless stones termed sapphire, with the colour as prefix. Star-stones (star ruby and star sapphire) show six-rayed star of light when cut *en cabochon* in the correct orientation, *i.e.* with the base of the stone at right angles to the vertical crystal axis. "Fancy sapphires" is the trade name applied to all colours of corundum except the red and blue. Emery is an impure form of corundum used as an abrasive. $H. = 9$, but rubies are in general slightly softer than sapphires. Cleavage is not apparent, but there is a "false cleavage" known as *parting* and due to secondary twinning. $S.G. = 3\cdot99$ ($3\cdot95$–$4\cdot05$). The lustre is vitreous and the refraction double. $R.I. = 1\cdot76$–$1\cdot77$, with a birefringence of $0\cdot008$. Dichroism is strong in ruby and blue sapphire and most fancy sapphires except the yellow. The whitish sheen seen in some rubies and sapphires is known as "silk." It is due to the presence of vast numbers of microscopically small canals reflecting the light. When these canals are in three directions parallel to the sides of the hexagonal form, stones cut *en cabochon* show the six-rayed star as mentioned above, *i.e.* asterism.

Corundum occurs in gravels and clays derived from an impure limestone, recrystallization being caused by the influence of heat and pressure. Finest rubies are found in Burma (Mogok), while rubies from Thailand (Siam) are browner and contain more iron. Ceylon produces pale ruby which merge into the variety known as "pink sapphire." A ruby of an unusual tinge of colour is found in large sizes in Tanzania (Tanganyika) where sapphires of various fancy colours are also found. Good rubies are found in Kenya and sapphires in Malawi. Fine sapphires are found in Thailand (Siam), Kashmir and Burma, while Ceylon produces good blue stones and many fancy colours. Blue sapphires from Australia are dark and inky and those from Montana (U.S.A.) have a distinctly metallic appearance. Rubies fluoresce strongly with a red glow when placed under ultra-violet light, due to chromic oxide (Cr_2O_3), and it is to this oxide that the red colour of the stone is due. The blue of the sapphire is caused by a trace of iron and titanium. (The synthetic corundum will be discussed later.)

BERYL

Silicate of aluminium and beryllium ($Be_3Al_2(SiO_3)_6$; Hexagonal, as hexagonal prisms. Varieties: grass-green (emerald), pale blue to bluish-green (aquamarine), yellow (golden beryl), pink (rose beryl or Morganite) and colourless. $H. =$ about $7\frac{3}{4}$, aquamarine is slightly harder than emerald. The cleavage is weak and indistinct. $S.G. =$ about $2 \cdot 7$. Full range for the species is $2 \cdot 65$ to $2 \cdot 85$ (emerald $2 \cdot 65$ to $2 \cdot 76$). The lustre is vitreous and the refraction double. $R.I. = 1 \cdot 57 - 1 \cdot 58$, with birefringence of about $0 \cdot 006$. Dichroism is strong in the emerald and some blue aquamarines but is weak in the other varieties.

Emerald is rarely found which is not badly flawed, while the aquamarine is found in large crystals perfectly water clear. The major occurrences of emerald are in Colombia (S. America), where it is found in veins of calcite; in the Ural Mountains (Russia); Egypt, in a mica schist; in Brazil; in Southern Rhodesia; India and Pakistan; in South Africa (Transvaal) and in Australia. Aquamarines are found in Brazil, California, Madagascar and Ceylon. Emerald, alone of the beryls, has been made synthetically for commercial cut stones. They are made in the United States of America, in France and in Germany.

TOPAZ

Fluo-silicate of aluminium ($Al_2(F, OH)_2SiO_4$); Orthorhombic crystals prismatic in habit, prism faces vertically striated, and capped with pyramids. Varieties: colourless (white topaz) and colours from yellow to brown are common. Blue to green, which resembles aquamarine, occurs. Red and pink colours are rarely found naturally, the pink topaz on the market is the brown variety treated with heat which turns the stone a lovely rose pink (or if incorrectly heated a salmon colour). This is termed "pinking." $H. = 8$. Topaz has a very strong cleavage at right angles to the length of the crystal, and sometimes the basal pinacoid. Owing to the substitution in varying amounts of the fluorine and the hydroxyl (OH) in the composition of topaz the constants are to some extent variable, but normally the jewellery topazes fall into two fairly well-defined groups:

	S.G.	R.I.	Biref.
Colourless, blue and some yellows	3·56	1·61–1·62	0·010
Yellow, brown and pink	3·53	1·63–1·64	0·008

The dichroism is distinct in well-coloured stones (strong in pink "fired" topaz). The principal localities for topaz are in Brazil, Russia and Ceylon. Lesser occurrences are in Saxony and Japan, while recent finds have been in South-west Africa, Northern Nigeria and Southern Rhodesia. Topaz is also found in Scotland and in the Mourne

Mountains in Ireland. As the name "topaz" has been used indiscriminately for many yellow stones, and in particular the yellow quartz (citrine), it is usual to refer to the true topaz as "Brazilian topaz."

SPINEL

Magnesium aluminate ($MgAl_2O_4$); Cubic, commonly as octahedra (8-sided). Twins common, particularly the type known as the "spinel twin." Varieties: reds, sometimes miscalled "Ruby Spinel," pale reds are known as "Balas Ruby," yellowish-red as Rubicelle ("Flame spinel"), purples, blues, both light and dark, greens and black. The dark green is known as chlorospinel and the black as pleonaste or ceylonite. $H. = 8$. Spinel shows practically no cleavage. $S.G. = 3 \cdot 60$. The lustre is vitreous and the refraction is single. $R.I. = 1 \cdot 72$. Ceylonites may reach a density of $3 \cdot 80$ and the refractive index to $1 \cdot 80$. Spinel is generally found in association with ruby in Burma and Thailand (Siam) and in the gem gravels of Ceylon. (The synthetic spinels will be discussed later.)

GARNET

This name is applied to a group of gemstones which crystallize in the cubic system as dodecahedra or icositetrahedra and which have a definite relation between their chemical compositions. All consist of a double silicate in which one of the metals may be calcium, iron, magnesium or manganese while the others may be aluminium, iron or chromium. Garnets are the classic example of isomorphous replacement, where ions of metals having similar ionic radii can interchange with one another to produce an *isomorphous series*. The garnets are divided into two groups: the *pyralspite* series which include the pyrope, almandine and spessartite garnets; and the *ugrandite* series formed by the uvarovite, grossularite and andradite garnets. The garnets in each series interchange isomorphously with one another, but there is little isomorphous interchange between the two groups.

Pyrope. Magnesium aluminium silicate $(Mg_3Al_2(SiO_4)_3)$; $H. = 7\frac{1}{2}$; $S.G. = 3\cdot68$ to $3\cdot8$; $R.I. = 1\cdot74$ to $1\cdot76$; Colour = blood-red; Localities = South Africa (in association with diamond), Bohemia, Arizona, etc. Pyropes of high S.G. and R.I. merge into almandine.

Almandine. Iron aluminium silicate $(Fe_3Al_2(SiO_4)_3)$; $H. = 7\frac{1}{2}$; $S.G. = 3\cdot8$ to $4\cdot20$; $R.I. = 1\cdot76$ to $1\cdot82$; Colours are deep red, violet-red to black; Localities for almandine are India, Ceylon, Australia and North and South America. Almandine exhibits a characteristic absorption spectrum of three strong bands, one in the yellow and two in the green. Some almandine shows 4 or 6-rayed asterism. The lower values of density and refractive index in almandine garnets are sometimes called *intermediate garnets* or *pyrope/almandine series*. The rhododendron-red garnet which is known by the name *rhodolite garnet* and has a density of $3\cdot84$ and refractive index of $1\cdot76$ is an intermediate garnet. Originally found in North Carolina, some large garnets of this type have come from Tanzania.

Spessartite. Manganese aluminium silicate $(Mn_3Al_2(SiO_4)_3)$; $H. = 7\frac{1}{4}$; $S.G. = 3\cdot90$ to $4\cdot20$; $R.I. = 1\cdot79$ to $1\cdot81$; Colour = orange-red and brown; Localities = Bavaria, Ceylon, Tyrol and U.S.A. The calcium chromium silicate garnet known as *Uvarovite* has not been found in pieces (crystals) large enough to cut, if it were it would make an attractive green stone. The hardness is $7\frac{1}{2}$ on Mohs's scale, the density $3\cdot77$ and the refractive index is $1\cdot87$.

Grossular. Calcium aluminium silicate $(Ca_3Al_2(SiO_4)_3)$; $H. = 6\frac{1}{2}$ to 7; $S.G. = 3\cdot55$ to $3\cdot67$; $R.I. = 1\cdot74$; Colours are brownish-yellow (Cinnamon stone) and reddish-orange (jacinth), both these varieties being known as *hessonite*. A massive green variety is known as "Transvaal jade." The most important locality for hessonite is Ceylon. The massive grossular, as its name implies, comes from South Africa, and is found in colours other than green. Also from South Africa, and from West Pakistan, have recently come some grossular garnets of an emerald green or yellowish-green colour.

A new and previously unknown variety of grossular garnet has been found in Kenya and Tanzania. The stones are transparent and can be pale yellowish-green to emerald green in colour, or a golden yellow. The green stones are said to be coloured by vanadium. The density is approximately 3·62, and the refractive index 1·74. Inclusions are few and the stones are remarkably clean so that they can be readily recognized from hessonite which is full of inclusions and swirls.

Andradite. Calcium iron silicate ($Ca_3Fe_2(SiO_4)_3$); $H. = 6\frac{1}{2}$; $S.G. = 3·84$. $R.I. = 1·89$; Colours = green (demantoid) and yellow (topazolite); Localities = Russia and Saxony. Andradite shows considerable "fire," greater even than that of the diamond. Demantoid shows an absorption spectrum of a band in the violet.

TOURMALINE

A complex boro-silicate of aluminium; Trigonal with prismatic habit. The crystals are roughly triangular in section capped with rhombohedra. The opposite ends of the crystal have different terminations (*hemimorphism*) and they are deeply striated along their length; Varieties: red (rubellite), blue (indicolite), green, yellow, violet-red; $H. = 7\frac{1}{4}$; $S.G. = 3·05$; $R.I. = 1·62-1·64$; the lustre is vitreous and the refraction double, about 0·018. Dichroism is strong; Localities = Brazil, Siberia, California, Madagascar and in the Ceylon gem gravels. A fibrous form of tourmaline gives a cat's eye effect. Various tourmalines, including a green stone which owes its colour to chromium and vanadium, and shows a red colour through the Chelsea colour filter, are found in Tanzania.

PERIDOT (THE OLIVINE OF SCIENCE)

Silicate of magnesium and iron ($(Mg, Fe)_2SiO_4$); Orthorhombic with prismatic habit (crystals are often flattened); Varieties: yellow, greenish-yellow, bottle-green, leaf-green and brown. $H. = 6\frac{1}{2}$ to 7; $S.G. = 3·34$; Lustre somewhat oily and refraction double (0·036); $R.I. = 1·66-1·70$. The dichroism is distinct; Localities = Island of St. John in the Red Sea, Burma, Australia and Norway.

ZIRCON

Silicate of zirconium ($ZrSiO_4$); Tetragonal, common form is a four-sided prism terminated at each end with a four-sided pyramid; Varieties: colourless, yellow, reds and reddish-browns, greens and many fancy colours. The popular blue and orange colours and the colourless stones now on the market are "fired" or, as it is sometimes termed, *heat treated*. The brown and hyacinth colours from Indo-China are the only crystals which are usable for this purpose. If the heating is carried out in air or with an excess of oxygen the colours formed are golden and colourless, while if the treatment is carried out in an atmosphere deficient in oxygen the blue colours are produced. Zircon is remarkable for its wide range of S.G. and R.I.; there is, in fact, not one zircon but three zircons, viz. the (*a*) or low type; the (*b*) or high type; and (*c*) the intermediate type.

(*a*) *Low type.*

Nearly amorphous, only found as rolled pebbles; $H. = 6$; $S.G. = 3.94$ to 4.40; $R.I. = 1.78$ to 1.84. Refraction; very nearly single; Dichroism none; Colours = green or greenish brown. Absorption spectrum shows only a smudged line at 6535A.

(*b*) *High type.*

Definite tetragonal crystals. $H. = 7\frac{1}{4}$; $S.G. = 4.65$ to 4.71; the refraction is double and large in amount; $R.I. = 1.92-1.98$; Dichroism weak, except in the heat-treated blue stones; Colours = colourless, red, blue, honey-yellow and light green.

(*c*) *Intermediate type.*

$S.G. = 4.10$ to 4.65; $R.I. = 1.84-1.85$ and higher. On heating this type it is converted to the high type with increase not only of S.G. and R.I., but also amount of double refraction.

It has been established that true zircon is the *high type*, and that the *low type* consists of more or less amorphous silica and zirconia and has been broken down from the high type by some form of radio-activity from elements isomorphous in the zircon, the intermediate type being those stones in which the breakdown of the crystal lattice has only partly occurred. Stones which show such a breakdown are termed *metamict*. Heat will often return these low-type zircons to the high type, but the common idea that the heat-treated zircons are low or intermediate types is a fallacy; these heat-treated stones are obtained from high-type brown crystals found in Indo-China. Zircon exhibits in many cases a characteristic absorption spectrum of fine lines, due to traces of uranium. There are many lines seen in Burma zircons, a less number in Ceylon stones, and in the heat-treated jewellery stones there may be seen only the 6535A line in the orange-red as a very sharp fine line. The localities in which this gemstone is found are Ceylon, Burma, Thailand (Siam), Indo-China, Australia, South Africa and France.

CHRYSOBERYL

Beryllium aluminate $(BeAl_2O_4)$; Orthorhombic, flattened twin crystals common, sometimes giving a pseudohexagonal form; Varieties: pale yellow to greenish-yellow, dark green (alexandrite) and honey-yellow to brownish-green with chatoyant effect (cat's-eye). Distinct cleavage in one direction only; $H. = 8\frac{1}{2}$; $S.G. = 3\cdot71$. Refraction is double and the dichroism while strong in alexandrite is weak in the other varieties. $R.I. = 1\cdot75-1\cdot76$. Alexandrite appears green in daylight and red in artificial light. Localities = Brazil (yellows), Ural Mountains, Russia (alexandrite), Ceylon (cat's-eyes and alexandrite), Rhodesia (alexandrite). The alexandrite variety of chrysoberyl is now made synthetically.

QUARTZ

Oxide of silicon (silica) (SiO_2) may be divided into two groups, the crystalline and the cryptocrystalline.

Crystalline type.

Trigonal, prismatic habit; Varieties: colourless (rock crystal), brown (smoky quartz), white (milky quartz), yellow to reddish-brown (cairngorm), yellow (citrine), purple (amethyst), pink (rose quartz), green (prase), green chatoyant (cat's-eye), yellow chatoyant (tiger's-eye), blue (siderite), brown, yellow, red or green with spangles of mica (aventurine), colourless with acicular inclusions (rutilated quartz or Venus' hair stone); $H. = 7$. $S.G. = 2·65$. Lustre is vitreous and refraction double while the dichroism is weak; $R.I. = 1·54–1·55$. Smoky quartz when heated reddish-brown and amethyst so treated turns to a yellow citrine. Rose quartz is noteworthy in never being found as crystals, only massive; "Tiger's-eye" is often termed *crocidolite*, which is the name applied to an asbestos, and it is the replacement by silica of the fibres of asbestos which give the "tiger's-eye." Quartz is found abundantly all over the world, the most important localities for gem material are Brazil, Ceylon, Russia Madagascar, Japan, Scotland, etc. (rock crystal, citrine and amethyst), India and China (aventurine) and Griqualand, S.W. Africa (crocidolite). A synthetic quartz is produced.

Crypto-crystalline type.

Composed of a mass of minute crystalline fibres. Chalcedony is the general term used for this type of quartz, variety names being given to the different colours, viz. *cornelian*, translucent flesh-red; *sard*, brownish-red; *chrysoprase*, translucent apple-green; *bloodstone*, dark green with scattered spots of red jasper; *agates and onyx* are banded varieties and *jasper* is an impure variety. $H. = 7$; $S.G. = 2·58$ to $2·64$ (slightly lower than crystalline quartz); $R.I. = 1·53–1·54$ (likewise slightly lower). Chalcedony is somewhat porous and, therefore, can be stained in various colours. Chalcedony is very widespread, the main localities are Brazil, Madagascar, Uruguay, etc. Moss agate, clear chalcedony containing inclusions in the form of ferns is a type commonly found in India. A green, chrome chalcedony, called "Mtorolite" is found in Rhodesia.

OPAL

Hydrated silica ($SiO_2 \, xH_2O$). Non-crystalline, hence amorphous, a solidified jelly. Varieties are *black opal* and *white opal*, both of which

show characteristic opalescent colours due to interference of light, as
has been explained. *Fire opal* is transparent to translucent and of
reddish-yellow colour. $H. = 5\frac{1}{2}$ to $6\frac{1}{2}$; $S.G. = 2\cdot1$. Refraction single
and $R.I. = 1\cdot45$. The old theory that the interference of light producing the play of colour in opal was due to thin films was never
confirmed. What was always uncertain was the nature of the "films"
in opal; however, recent experiments by Australian workers using
electron microscopy have shown that these "films" are structual and
consist essentially of minute spherical particles of amorphous silica in
close-packed regular arrangement. It is to this structure and the size
of the spherical particles that the interference effects by diffraction of
the incident rays of white light produce the play of colour in opal.
Opal is found in Hungary, Australia (black and white) and Mexico
(fire opal), and Nevada, U.S.A. Some opal matrix from Andamooka,
South Australia, is dyed black by a process which is analogous to that
used for the production of black onyx.

TURQUOISE

Hydrous phosphate of aluminium coloured by a copper compound;
Triclinic (crypto-crystalline) as nodules or concretionary masses and
veins in sedimentary rocks. Colours blue and green. Turquoise is
semi-translucent to opaque and valued for its body colour only.
$H. = 6$; $S.G. = 2\cdot6$ to $2\cdot8$; $R.I.$ about $1\cdot62$. Lustre is waxy. May be
identified by the absorption bands in the blue part of the spectrum.
Best turquoise comes from Persia, other localities being Sinai
Peninsula, Egypt, Tibet and New Mexico. When turquoise is cut
with some of the limonite matrix it is known as *turquoise matrix*.

Turquoise is not an easy gemstone to identify, for apart from other
natural materials which can be confused with it, such as *variscite*,
wardite and the stained fossil bone called *odontolite*, much American
turquoise is bonded with silica or plastic in order to make it more solid
and less chalky so that it may be fashioned. There are also a number
of artificial products having similar constituents to turquoise made,
such as the so-called "Viennese turquoise." The white mineral *howlite*

is dyed blue and makes a fine turquoise simulant. Some "turquoise" is just a glass imitation.

SPODUMENE

Silicate of aluminium and lithium ($LiAl(SiO_3)_2$); Monoclinic with prismatic habit; Varieties: yellow, green (hiddenite) and lilac (kunzite). $H. = 6\frac{1}{2}$; $S.G. = 3·18$. Cleavage perfect in two directions, lustre vitreous and refraction double. $R.I. = 1·66–1·68$ and exhibits strong dichroism. Localities are California and Madagascar (kunzite and yellow), N. Carolina (hiddenite), Brazil (hiddenite, kunzite and yellow).

SPHENE

Silicate and titanate of calcium ($CaTiSiO_5$); Monoclinic; Colour varieties: green, yellow and brownish-yellow. $H. = 5\frac{1}{2}$; $S.G. = 3·53$. Lustre adamantine, refraction double and dichroism very strong. $R.I. = 1·91–2·06$. Sphene exhibits greater "fire" than the diamond. Found in Burma, Switzerland and Baja California, Mexico.

FELDSPAR

Silicate of aluminium with another metal which may be either potassium, sodium or calcium. Two groups: (a) orthoclase = potassium feldspar; (b) plagioclase = sodium and calcium feldspars. Orthoclase crystallizes in the monoclinic system and plagioclase in the triclinic system. The varieties are as follows:

Moonstone. A monoclinic orthoclase feldspar of bluish-white colour and having a milky sheen; the effect being termed *adularescence*. The interference effect being restricted to a certain colour owing to the regularity of the lamellae which are probably caused through intergrowths of the albite molecule. The density is 2·56; the *R.I.* 1·52 to 1·53 with a birefringence of 0·008, and the hardness is 6 on Mohs's scale. It is found in Ceylon, Burma, India and Madagascar.

Yellow orthoclase. A transparent variety of orthoclase of a clear yellow colour which is due to iron. The *S.G.* and *R.I.* (2·58 and 1·54 respectively) are a little higher than for moonstone, but the double refraction of 0·005 is lower, and by this it may be separated from the yellow quartz. Madagascar is the source of this type.

Microcline (*"Amazon stone"*) is a potassium feldspar which crystallizes in the triclinic system, but it is not far off the monoclinic angle, hence the name. The jewellery material is green or bluish green in colour. $S.G. = 2·56$; $R.I. = 1·53$; $H. = 6\frac{1}{4}$, and the material is at best only translucent. The localities are Colorado, U.S.A., where it is found in fine crystal groups, Canada, India, Rhodesia, Brazil and Russia.

Sunstone. A plagioclase feldspar (oligoclase) which has a reddish colour and spangled effect due to the inclusion of masses of platy crystals of an iron mineral. The density averages 2·64 and the $R.I. = 1·54$. The hardness is about $6\frac{1}{4}$ to $6\frac{1}{2}$ on Mohs's scale. The sunstone variety of feldspar is found in Norway and Canada.

Labradorite is a greyish feldspar which shows iridescent flashes of colour which is referred to as interference at thin films of repeated twinning; the effect being known as *labradorescence*. The $S.G.$ is 2·70, the $R.I. = 1·56$ and the hardness about $6\frac{1}{2}$. The rock-like iridescent material is found in Canada and elsewhere; there being an attractive source in Finland. The name *spectrolite* being applied to it. Pale yellow transparent labradorite is found in Utah, U.S.A. and in Mexico; and in Madagascar there is a transparent labradorite showing a play of colour. *Black moonstone* is a labradorite with a bluish flash and which shows a cat's-eye effect when cut in the cabochon style.

JADE

Two distinct minerals are known under this name.

Nephrite.

A tough compact fibrous mineral varying in colour from white to dark green; $H. = 6$ to $6\frac{1}{2}$; $S.G. = 2·95$ to $3·1$. Used for carvings and found in New Zealand, Turkestan, Russia, U.S.A. and Rhodesia.

Jadeite.

The most highly prized of the two "jades" is a similarly compact mineral showing a range of colour from white to green and also brown, red, mauve, etc. It is the material most prized by the Chinese for their carvings; $H. = 6\frac{1}{2}$ to 7; $S.G. = 3 \cdot 3$ to $3 \cdot 5$. Jadeite is found in Burma. This ornamental stone is also found in small quantities in Japan, California and in Guatemala. Polished specimens are characterized by the mottling of the surface due to the uneven polishing of the granules which make up the stone.

The jades are imitated by a number of other natural minerals, the most prominent being the bowenite variety of serpentine which is sold under the misnomer "New jade." Massive grossular garnet, massive green idocrase, some chrysoprase and some green aventurine quartz imitate jade. Some jadeite is stained to give a better colour.

LAPIS LAZULI

Chief character is its colour, a uniform dark blue of great intensity (often containing glistening flakes of yellow iron pyrites). It is really a mixture of different minerals (hauynite, lazurite and sodalite) grains of which are in a matrix of calcite. $S.G. = 2 \cdot 7$ to $2 \cdot 9$. Localities are Afghanistan, Chile, Siberia and California.

Lapis lazuli is imitated by a stained jasper ("Swiss lapis"), and by a type of sintered synthetic blue spinel.

ZOISITE

Calcium aluminium silicate ($HCa_2Al_3Si_3O_{13}$); Orthorhombic with prismatic habit; Varieties, sapphire-blue, and brownish. $H. = 6\frac{1}{2}$; $S.G. = 3 \cdot 35$; $R.I. = 1 \cdot 69 – 1 \cdot 70$ with double refraction of $0 \cdot 009$. Strongly pleochroic (blue; purplish red and yellow). These new sapphire blue crystals come from Tanzania and hence the cut stones are called "tanzanite". The pink massive ornamental stone called Thulite is also a zoisite (see page 195).

SYNTHETIC GEMS

SINCE the dawn of chemical science as an exact art, in the eighteenth century, attempts have been made to produce exact copies of the minerals and crystals found in God's good earth. The production of those minerals which are prized by man for their rarity, and by woman as a foil to her own rare charm and beauty, has acted as a spur to the man of science in his varied attempts to bridle nature, and his success in this direction forms the subject of these few notes.

While, unknown to the average jeweller and layman, for many years experiments on the synthesis of gemstones have been carried out in laboratories throughout the world, at the present time it may be safely stated that every gemstone has been made synthetically. There is, however, the consideration that to be of commercial importance the man-made gem must be cheaper to produce than the natural mined stone and in crystals large enough for cutting: *e.g.* the mineral quartz (SiO_2) has been successfully synthetically produced for many years, but quartz, even in the more highly prized variety—amethyst —is so abundant in nature that the cost of making, in a laboratory is far greater than the value it would have in the market.

While this remains true of most gem materials, with the so-called precious stones, that is, the diamond, the ruby, the emerald and the sapphire, the economic conditions give every encouragement for the synthetic production on a commercial basis. It is in the main the commercially produced synthetic gems which concern the jeweller and practical gemmologist.

With its simple chemical composition (carbon $= C.$), diamond should apparently be the easiest mineral to produce synthetically, but in the case of this gem its synthesis is wellnigh impossible owing to the fact that carbon burns at a temperature less than its melting point. Moreover, the stable form of carbon is the common mineral graphite.

The first attempt to make diamond was that of J. B. Hannay, a Glasgow chemist, who, in 1880, heated in a strong sealed cylinder a mixture of hydrocarbons and the rare element lithium. The resulting hard black mass was found to contain a few minute crystals whose size precluded any attempt, with the means then available, accurately to identify them. Henri Moissan, whose experiments have assumed classic importance, heated a mixture of iron and sugar carbon contained in a carbon crucible to about 4,000° C. in an electric furnace. The iron melted and became saturated with carbon. The mixture was rapidly cooled by being placed in molten lead. This formed a crust on the outside with the more slowly solidifying material in the centre still molten. Iron, like ice, expands on assuming the solid state from the liquid, thus, when the centre does solidify it does so under great pressure. The iron was laboriously dissolved out by warm aqua regia (a mixture of hydrochloric and nitric acids) and the residue examined. This was found to consist in the main of carbon in the form of graphite and a few small and distorted crystals which were assumed, with the aid of tests then available, to be diamond. Moissan, who carried out these experiments in 1893, was led to follow this line of investigation by the discovery of diamond in iron meteorites. That diamonds were produced by these experiments is still open to question.

Following on the work of P. W. Bridgman in the United States of America who worked out the theoretical considerations that for the forming of diamond high temperatures and high pressures would be needed, in 1955 there was a successful production of minute diamond crystals by the General Electric Company at Schenectady, U.S.A. There is, however, a world of difference between an academic production of minute crystals and gems for the jeweller, who can rest assured that no diamonds synthetically made can come his way for a generation or two. Despite the small sizes of the diamonds produced, they do have a use in the making of diamond powders for polishing and grinding. So much so that other factories are now producing synthetic diamonds, including one in Ireland.

With the corundum gems—ruby and sapphire—considerable success has been obtained. As early as 1837 the French chemist, Marc A. A. Gaudin, produced a few tiny flakes of crystallized alumina, while E. Fremy and C. Feil, in 1877, produced similar and larger plate-like crystals of ruby. In 1885 a number of rubies came upon the jewellery market and were accepted as natural stones. Soon their genuineness was questioned, and it later transpired that these stones had been made by the direct fusion of small fragments of real ruby, with a small piece of bichromate of potash to give the colour, in the flame of an oxy-hydrogen blowpipe. These stones, which had all the optical and physical characters of true ruby, were seen, when viewed under a lens, to contain many gas bubbles, often irregularly arranged and giving the stone a cloudy effect. They often contain flaws due to the rapid cooling, and some show the characteristic whirl striæ like that seen in badly annealed glass. Later, in 1895, Michaud improved the method by heating a large fragment of natural ruby at about 1,800° C. in a revolving platinum crucible and slowly adding smaller chips, sometimes with a little potassium bichromate to increase the colour. These gems may be said to be a form of reconstruction, and are known as *reconstructed rubies*. It must be mentioned that there are no reconstructed sapphires.

After some years of research the French chemist, Auguste Verneuil, discovered a method whereby true synthetic corundum of all colours and of large size could be made by a "flame fusion" method. He constructed a special form of inverted oxy-hydrogen blowpipe or *chalumeau*, and in 1904 published a short account of his experiments.

The apparatus used by Verneuil consists of a vertical blowpipe (fig. 46), whose upper part is in the form of a large chamber in which is suspended a sieve containing the finely powdered mixture of alumina and colouring oxide (chromium oxide for ruby). This sieve is mechanically vibrated at a rate of between eighty and twenty times

PLATE I

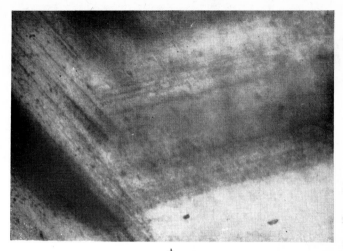

A

ANGULAR ZONING FORMED OF FINE "SILK" IN A NATURAL RUBY

B

LIQUID-FILLED "FEATHERS" IN A YELLOW SAPPHIRE

PLATE II

A

VARIOUS TYPES OF GAS BUBBLES AND A BUBBLE CLOUD WITH CURVED
STRUCTURE LINES IN A SYNTHETIC RUBY

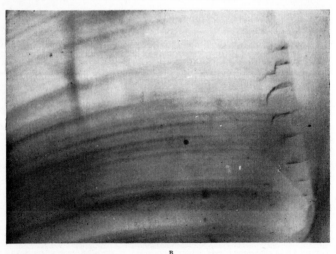

B

CURVED COLOUR BANDS AND BUBBLES IN A SYNTHETIC SAPPHIRE. THERE ARE "FIRE
MARKS" ALONG ONE FACET EDGE WHICH ARE ONLY SEEN IN CORUNDUM

PLATE III

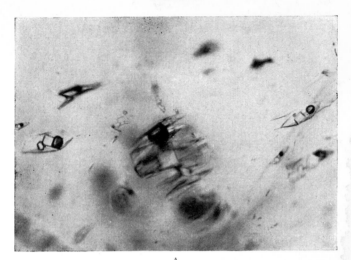

A

THREE-PHASE INCLUSIONS IN A COLOMBIAN EMERALD

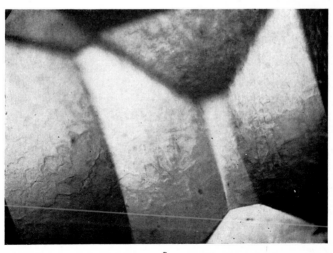

B

EX-SOLUTION OF CALCITE IN A NATURAL EMERALD

PLATE IV

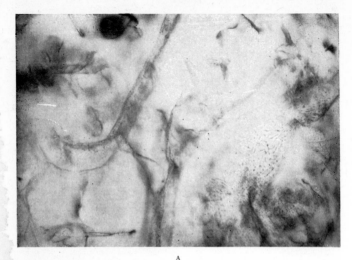

A

"FEATHERS" IN A SYNTHETIC EMERALD

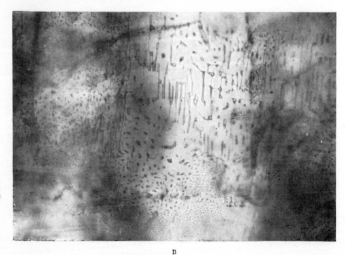

B

"FEATHERS" IN A SYNTHETIC EMERALD

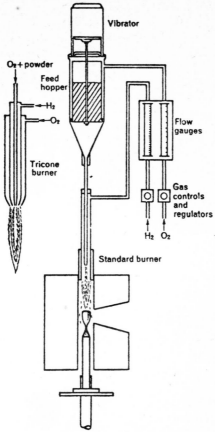

FIG. 46.—The Verneuil furnace (with inset the tricone burner used for titanium synthetics).

per minute in order to release the powder in discrete amounts. Oxygen enters the blowpipe through a pipe at the upper end of the chamber and this current of oxygen carries the released powder with it down the inner tube of the furnace. An outer annular tube carries hydrogen and the ends of the two tubes form a nozzle at which point the gases are ignited producing a downward pointing flame. The powder on passing through the flame melts and falls on a ceramic pedestal, called a *candle*. The fused alumina solidifies on the end of the candle, forming a cone of inverted pear-shaped "blobs," one of which, by control of the rate of powder dropped and pressure of the gases, is allowed to grow, the tip of this growing *stalagmite* being kept in the hottest part of the flame by adjustment of the height of the candle.

The clear mass which grows on the support is known as a *boule* or *birne*, and is pear-shape in form, the stalk being the part attached to the stand. The top of the mass is seen to be covered with a reticulated "froth" which under magnification is seen to consist of a mass of crystal plates. The actual corundum boule is one single crystal individual, but has a line of weakness, due to a twin plane, which causes the boule to split in two pieces vertically from top to bottom when struck by a blow or when the stalk is nipped off with pliers.

Stones cut from these boules have all the physical and optical properties of a natural stone, that is, they have the same specific gravity and refractive indices as natural corundum, and they also exhibit dichroism. They are made in all the colours in which natural stones are found. If only pure alumina is used, "white" sapphire is made; the red of ruby is obtained by the addition to the alumina of about 2·5 per cent of chromic oxide; while for sapphire the oxides of titanium and iron are used as the colouring oxides, and other oxides are used for other colours.

As has been mentioned, these synthetic corundums are made in many different colours, and it may be of some value if a list of colours and the gems they simulate is appended:

Red	...	...	...	Ruby.
Dark Red	...	...	...	Garnet.
Rose red	...	...	...	Pink Sapphire, "Fired" Topaz, etc.
Lilac	...	...	...	Kunzite.
Purple	...	...	...	Amethyst, Violet Sapphire.

Yellow ...	...	...	...	Yellow Sapphire, Topaz, etc.
Orange ...	...	...	...	Yellow Sapphire.
Orange red	...	...	...	Garnet, Zircon, Fire Opal, etc.
Blue ...	...	...	...	Sapphire.
Green ...	...	...	...	Sapphire, Emerald, etc.
Brown ...	...	...	...	Topaz.
Green (with colour change)		...		Alexandrite.

Since the Second World War there have been produced in America synthetic corundums with asteriated effect. These synthetic star rubies and sapphires show closely spaced needles (of titanium oxide) arranged at 60°, but also show the typical curved structure lines and gas bubbles of the normal synthetic corundum.

Despite the fact that synthetic corundum has almost every character of the natural gem corundum there are yet structural differences which allow the discrimination between the natural and man-made gems. These differences, sometimes easily visible with the aid of a low power hand lens, are in general only observed by the aid of the more powerful and all-seeing eye of the microscope. It may be as well to recall that in order to "get into" the stone it may be necessary to immerse it in highly refractive oil, such as monobromonaphthalene. A natural stone almost invariably shows some signs of its natural origin, such as straight lines crossing one another at an angle of 60° or crystal inclusions, which always show straight sides. The synthetic corundum shows curved lines or bands of growth and often round gas bubbles which, if small, may appear as clouds of dust spots. In coloured material the curved lines are most characteristic. The natural stone invariably shows the hall mark of its natural origin, in fact, it is extremely rare to find a natural corundum which does not show some characteristic sign; either in the way of large crystal inclusions, small needle-like crystals which are oriented at 60°, or straight lines or bands. The synthetic corundums of today are comparatively *clean*, and the large gas bubbles seen in the earlier types are absent, although the curved lines of the growth of the boule are generally visible if care and patience is taken with the examination.

After Verneuil's initial success with the production of the synthetic red corundum, an attempt was made to make the blue sapphire. It was at that time thought that cobalt was the metal which gave the blue colour to this variety of corundum, hence cobalt was used with the alumina in the first experiments. The resultant boule was found to be patchy in colour, which, indeed, scarcely simulated the colour of the natural sapphire. In order to make the colour more uniform the experimenters added magnesia to the alumina and cobalt. The result was a good clean stone of uniform colour, which had a characteristic "Reckitt's blue" rather than the colour of the natural blue of the sapphire. This was not all, for on examination the stone was found to be a spinel and not a corundum.

At the time, about 1907, there was no apparent necessity for the production of synthetic spinel. Spinel, even in the red variety, had no great value as a gemstone. In the last thirty years, those years in which more regard has been paid to such gemstones as blue zircon, aquamarine and pink topaz, etc., the synthesis of spinel by the Verneuil method has taken on a new importance by the facility with which the shades of these gemstones may be obtained in the synthetic spinel.

The boule obtained by the Verneuil synthetic spinel, although pear-shape in form like the similarly made corundum, has one difference in that the boules have flattened sides, the sides of a cube and the outward expression of the crystal structure (the synthetic corundum boule has been seen to show the hexagonal form, but this is very rare). Likewise the spinel differs from that of the corundum in that in many cases, particularly in the new colours, the molecular ratio is in general $MgO.2Al_2O_3$, whereas normal spinel is $MgO.Al_2O_3$. This difference is manifest in a slightly higher refractive index, i.e. 1·73 as against 1·72 for the natural stones. The specific gravity is also affected and is slightly higher, about 3·63.

Unlike synthetic corundum the synthetic spinel never shows curved bands or striæ and is remarkably free from gas bubbles. Their detection is easy, however, for the spinels are rarely made in colours reminiscent of the natural spinel. As before mentioned, all stones with a higher R.I. than the natural spinel must be suspect. The types of blue spinels made to imitate the blue zircon and the aquamarine are coloured with cobalt which causes the stone to assume a red or orange hue when it is viewed through the dichromatic filter (the Chelsea Colour Filter); the natural blue zircon and the aquamarine appear green when so viewed. The blue colours of synthetic spinel show the typical absorption spectrum of cobalt coloration; that is three broad bands in the orange-red, yellow and green parts of the spectrum. No natural mineral shows this absorption spectrum. Synthetic spinels may be convincingly identified by the peculiar anomalous double refraction shown by them when they are viewed between crossed polars. This is "tabby extinction" as it was named by Anderson.

A list of the colours in which the synthetic spinel is made is appended:

Red (rarely); pale blue ; dark blue; yellow and yellow-green; colourless; rose-red; deep green; and green with colour change (made to imitate the alexandrite).

The synthetic red spinels, of which small stones have been placed on the market, differ from the usual synthetic spinels in that they are equimolecular and do not have the excess alumina. The boules easily crack so that only small stones can be cut from them. They usually show strong curved lines and also show more of a ruby type fluorescence spectrum and not the "organ-pipe" spectrum shown by natural red spinels, and they generally have a refractive index of $1 \cdot 722$. Other special types of synthetic spinel are a white (colourless) spinel which has been heated to give a "schillerization" so that these stones imitate the moonstone, and there is a sintered cobalt-rich spinel made to imitate the lapis lazuli. These stones have a refractive index of $1 \cdot 725$ and a density of $3 \cdot 52$.

In comparatively recent times new synthetic gemstones have been produced on a modified type of Verneuil blowpipe. These stones are: *synthetic rutile*, a stone which is rarely found sufficiently clear in nature to cut as gemstones; and *strontium titanate*, which is a stone with no counterpart in nature.

Synthetic rutile (TiO_2) is a tetragonal mineral which is synthetically produced in a number of colours, such as orange, red, brown and blue, but the most common is a very pale yellowish white. These stones have a hardness of about 6; a density of 4·25 and refractive indices of 2·62–2·90 with the large double refraction of 0·287. These stones have about six times as much dispersion as the diamond, and the stones show so much "fire" that they tend to have the appearance of opals. *Strontium titanate* ($SrTiO_3$) is a colourless stone of the cubic system. It has a hardness of 6, a density of 5·13 and a single refraction of 2·41. The stone, which is one of the best simulants of diamond, has a dispersion of about four times as much as is seen in diamond. Strontium titanate is often marketed under the name FABULITE.

The synthesis of both these titanium minerals posed problems, for titanium oxide tends to lose oxygen when near its melting point; so in order to overcome this a modified Verneuil furnace is used. This furnace has a *tricone* burner which allows an outer envelope of oxygen to surround the flame. Even so, the boules of rutile and strontium titanate are black in colour when they come from the furnace and need to be annealed in a stream of oxygen before becoming clear and transparent.

Owing to its complex chemical composition, and the facility with which the molecules of alumina, beryllia and silica can assume different proportions and hence many different minerals, the synthesis of emerald has presented countless difficulties which have only been overcome during the past few decades.

Early experiments on the *reconstruction* of the green beryl on the lines of the reconstructed ruby failed. The resulting product being a glass and not a crystal. Emeralds of minute size had been made in the laboratories of experimental chemists for some time past but these had no commercial significance. In 1934–35 the German Dye Trust (I.G. Farbenindustrie) laboratories at their Bitterfeld works produced true synthetic emerald, and since 1940 synthetic emeralds have been produced in the United States of America, France and Germany.

Unlike the synthetic corundum and spinel just discussed, the synthetic emerald is not made by a flame fusion process; although recently a fairly successful growth by this means has been carried out in the United States of America the method has not been commercially acceptable. There are two methods which may be used for growing synthetic emerald crystals, that is the *hydrothermal method* and the *flux melt method*, both of which are basically the same, and both produce crystals which are hexagonal prisms like those found in nature. The hydrothermal method depends upon the fact that water at a high pressure will boil at a much greater temperature than the 100° C. at normal atmospheric pressures. At pressures of 100 atmospheres water can have the temperature of 400° C. and can then dissolve substances, such as the silicates. This will produce a supersaturated solution when the solution cools and then the mineral constituent will come out of the solution and form crystals on a suitable surface, such as a "seed" crystal. The operation being carried out in a "pressure bomb" called an *autoclave* (fig. 47). The method is slow but large crystals can be grown. The flux-melt method allows the growth to be as much as ten times faster. In this case the source material is dissolved in a suitable crucible in a suitable solvent (fig. 48), sufficient heat to fuse the material being used which, on cooling, separates out as crystals.

The characters of the synthetic emeralds so far on the market—those grown by Carroll F. Chatham of San Francisco, by Gilson of France and by Zerfass of Germany (the reported synthesis by the Linde Company of the United States have not at the time of writing been released commercially and cannot as yet be assessed)—show that the density is near 2·65 and the refractive index to be 1·56 with a double refraction of 0·003. All these constants are lower than for the natural emerald and allow identification of the synthetic emeralds. These synthetics, owing to their mode of growth, show natural-like inclusions in the form of "feathers" of two-phase inclusions which meander through the stone like twisted veils. They may show small crystals of phenacite, but the overall pattern is one not seen in natural

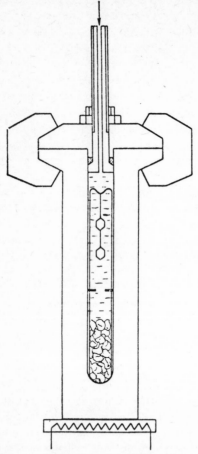

FIG. 47.—Hydrothermal growth autoclave.

emeralds and is characteristic of the synthetic emerald. All these synthetic emeralds show a strong red when viewed through the

Chelsea colour filter and between *crossed filters*. They show a red glow on irradiation by ultra-violet light, an exception being that the French manufacture by Gilson shows an orange glow.

Another type of stone which could be referred to as a synthetic stone is the "emerald-coated beryl" produced during 1960 by

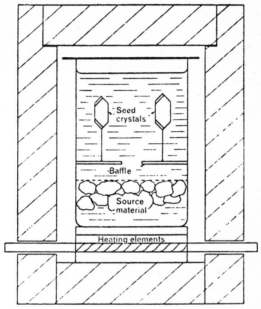

FIG. 48.—The flux-melt crucible.

Lechleitner of Austria. This stone is formed by growing by hydro-thermal means a surface of synthetic emerald on an already cut and polished pale-coloured natural beryl. Owing to the variation of the constants of the beryl used the density may vary. The density, usually about 2·69 to 2·71, may indeed be higher if the natural beryl used is higher, as it sometimes is in the case of some colourless and pale pink beryls. It may then reach to 2·80 or over; 1·57–1·58 are the values of refractive index found with this stone. Careful examination of this stone, to which the name Emerita has been applied, will show the *crazing* pattern in the surface layer. The inclusions, too, while they are those of beryl are not those of emerald.

A number of other crystals have been grown synthetically and some of these have now entered the gem market. Quartz has been grown in large colourless crystals which, as far as is known, are not cut into gemstones, but such crystals coloured by cobalt (blue) and iron (green) have been met with commercially. Other synthetically grown crystals which have been cut as gemstones, are scheelite; lithium niobate ("linobate"), YAGs, which are lithium aluminium garnets which are made in colourless ("diamonair") and in other colours, in particular a green which can resemble the demantoid garnet. The YAG stones can often be identified by their striking "rare earth" absorption spectra. Recently a successful synthesis of gem alexandrite has been made and the stones marketed. They have similar constants to the natural stones but may be identified by their typical "veil-like" inclusions.

In recent years, gadolinium gallium garnet (generally referred to as G.G.G.) has been marketed under the name "Galliant" as a simulant for diamond. The chemical formula is $Gd_3Ga_5O_{12}$, the hardness about $6\frac{1}{2}$. The refractive index is 2·03 and the density 7·05. These stones fluoresce with a straw yellow to peach colour. Other synthetic materials produced recently are synthetic turquoise, synthetic opal and synthetic lapis lazuli. Certain aspects of their structure allow them to be identified.

IMITATION GEMS

IN the last lesson there were discussed those gems which are made by man, which have the same chemical composition and similar physical and optical properties to the natural stones. The next types of counterfeit to come under review are those artificial stones which simulate the real gem in colour and appearance alone. Unlike the synthetic gems, which are a product of the scientific ingenuity of the nineteenth- and twentieth-century chemist, these imitation gems have been produced from mediæval and even ancient times, for, according to Flinders Petrie, glass was made in Egypt as early as 1600 B.C.

GLASS

Probably the most important imitation gem is that which is made of glass. Glass is a melt consisting in the main of sand (silica = SiO_2) and either soda or potash with the addition of other oxides (such as the oxides of barium, zinc, aluminium, thallium, etc.) and the colouring is produced by small amounts of other metallic oxides, certain elements and chemical compounds. Glass may best be defined as a mixture of silicates. It is amorphous, that is, non-crystalline; thus its physical and optical properties are the same in all directions. Glass, owing to the variable nature of its constituents, may therefore have an immense range of specific gravity and refractive index, although they do have some relation one to another. If, however, a glass has a definite chemical composition its constants will have a fixed value. This is so in the case of quartz glass and beryl glass, which are crystal quartz or beryl fused in a furnace, thus losing their crystalline structure and becoming a glass. The R.I. and S.G. of fused quartz (silica glass) are 1·46 and 2·21 respectively, while those of beryl glass are 1·525 and 2·40. These, as will be seen, are somewhat lower than for the crystal, and what is more important, the quartz and beryl glasses are singly refractive to light.

There are two main divisions into which glass may be divided, and these are known as *Crown (window or bottle) glass* and *Flint or lead glass.* Crown glass may be generally stated to be composed of silica, potash or soda and lime. It has a range of refractive index from about 1·44

	Refractive index.	Specific gravity.
Opal	1·44 to 1·46	2·07 to 2·15
Titanium-iron	1·47 to 1·49	2·40 to 2·52
Borosilicate	1·50	2·36
Calcium	1·52 to 1·54	2·53 to 2·57
Calcium-iron	1·57 to 1·59	2·66 to 2·75
Flint (Lead)	1·58 to 1·68	3·15 to 4·15

The above Table, based on the work of Mr. F. A. Bannister, M.A., is the range most usually found for the different types of glasses in use as gem counterfeits. The single figure given for the borosilicate glass must be taken as a mean. Not all borosilicate glasses have this as a constant figure.

to 1·53, and specific gravity from 2·05 to 2·60 (*the low figures relate to the opal glasses which may not be actually a true crown glass type, but for convenience may be classed with them*). The barium crown glasses rise above these figures and have a range of S.G. of between 2·87 and 3·66. These are often classed in the second or flint glass group. This group, the flint glasses, contains silica, potash or soda and lead oxide which increases the brilliancy and dispersion. These glasses have a range of R.I. of between 1·51 and 1·80 and over, while the S.G. varies between 2·56 to over 6 (*refractometer dense glasses are flint glasses, dense lead glasses, having a refractive index up to 1·96*). The specific gravity rises in conformity with the R.I. The figures given are the full ranges of the two types, but with imitation gemstones the ranges are much closer, viz.: Crown glasses = R.I. 1·52 to 1·54, S.G. 2·53 to 2·57, and for flint glasses = R.I. 1·58 to 1·68, S.G. 3·15 to 4·15.

As will be seen with the figures for the complete range, the constants overlap one another to a small extent. A better classification, depending on the composition, divides the glasses into definite groups. The table on p. 136 gives some indication of these glass families and their constants.

The colour of a glass imitation gemstone is produced by the inclusion during manufacture of some chemical element or compound, which in the case of the lead glasses needs to be small in amount and does not materially alter the physical and optical constants. A short table showing some of the more important colouring compounds (or elements) under the colours they produce is on page 138. Combinations of two colourings are possible and conditions of melt have considerable influence in determining the precise shade.

Opaque stones such as turquoise require the use of opacifiers beside the use of colouring compounds. The strong apple-green fluorescence seen with many paste stones, generally yellow-green colours, and usually attributed to uranium, must not be taken as conclusive evidence that the glass does contain uranium, as manganese in certain states also produces this rather spectacular fluorescence when the stone is bathed in ultra-violet light (*this remark may also apply to the synthetic spinel of yellow-green colour*).

There is one characteristic of nearly all glasses, that is, the low degree of hardness of paste stones, less than six, except in the case of certain *case-hardened* types. All these ordinary pastes, therefore, yield to an ordinary file, a test given in every text-book, despite that as a test it should be decried. A student often feels at a loss when dealing with paste stones by the use of instruments, although pastes are singly refractive to light, and hence monochroic, some doubt may still be felt, especially with colourless stones and those with weak or no dichroism. Again the refractive index may appear, in white light, to have the index of a gemstone which the paste may simulate. To this end some remarks, and some figures, may be given which may help in an easier and more accurate distinction.

Violets and Mauves, Purples, etc. ...	Manganese or nickel, in potash glasses.
Blues	Cobalt.
Blue-green ...	Copper, or iron in the reducing condition.
Green	Sesquioxide of chromium, iron in the ferrous state.
Green-yellow ...	Chromium compounds; uranium compounds (fluorescent); iron in reducing condition.
Yellows	Silver salts; Titanium compounds; Cadmium sulphide; Sulphur, also combination of iron and manganese.
Brown-yellows ...	Sulphur with carbon; iron oxide; Uranium in quantity.
Browns	Iron; Nickel, when in soda glass.
Pinks	Selenium, under certain conditions.
Reds	Copper with controlled reducing conditions (brilliant ruby); Selenium compounds or the element itself (ruby glass with orange tint); Gold (ruby with a purplish tint which is sometimes corrected with the addition of silver); Iron oxides in the ferric state.
Smoke tints ...	Platinium or iridium.

If it is possible to obtain determinations of both the refractive index and the specific gravity of a suspected paste stone, little confusion can arise, for the combined values have in general no similarity to those of a real stone. With topaz and beryl, and natural gemstones with constants of similar value, this generalization may not strictly be true; for example, a paste stone of pale blue colour having values of refractive index and specific gravity of 1·615 and 3·52 respectively could be a blue topaz with these figures (*it is inferred that the refractive index observations would, as in ordinary testing work, be made in white light; if monochromatic light, or a spinel refractometer were used, the double*

refraction would be apparent if the stone was a topaz). Anyway specific
gravity determinations are not easily performed in the general routine
work of business and a discussion of other tests which may be more

Colour.	R.I.	S.G.	Type of glass.
Sherry-brown ...	1·48	2·42	Calcium, titanium and iron.
Pale blue	1·50	2·36	Borosilicate.
Cobalt blue ...	1·51	2·47	Calcium glass.
Brownish-yellow ...	1·515	2·44	Calcium glass.
Uranium-green ...	1·515	2·48	Calcium glass.
Lemon yellow ...	1·53	2·56	Calcium glass.
Smoky colour ...	1·53	2·60	Calcium glass.
Sage green... ...	1·57	2·67	Calcium iron glass.
Sea blue	1·585	2·63	Calcium iron glass.
Amethyst colour ...	1·57	3·38	Lead glass.
Red...	1·58	3·18	Lead glass.
Pale blue	1·615	3·52	Lead glass.
Pale yellow ...	1·62	3·56	Lead glass.
Red...	1·63	3·75	Lead glass.
Rose red	1·63	3·71	Lead glass.
Green	1·635	3·74	Lead glass.
Colourless	1·635	3·78	Lead glass.
Dark red	1·64	3·74	Lead glass.
Dark purple ...	1·64	3·76	Lead glass.
Colourless	1·64	3·75	Lead glass.
Pale blue	1·64	3·71	Lead glass.
Sapphire blue ...	1·645	3·80	Lead glass.
Peridot green ...	1·67	4·12	Lead glass.
Pink	1·68	4·07	Lead glass.
Pink	1·69	4·20	Lead glass.

convenient are indicated. Before leaving the subject of the R.I. and
S.G. of glass, it may be of interest to note that of a test parcel of
ninety-five paste stones, all were found to have refractive indices lying
within the range of 1·48 to 1·69, and colour did not appear to have

any particular bearing on the R.I. value; however, it showed that it was rare to find a red paste with an R.I. below 1·62 and also that the reds, with the pinks and some peridot-greens, showed the highest figures, viz., 1·67 to 1·69. Likewise the table on p. 139 shows the combined values of a series of typical paste stones, and may do more to show what values one may expect to find in glass imitation gems, than pages of wordy discourse.

Glass, as in the case of the synthetic gems, shows under the microscope the unnatural nature of its formation due to the comparatively rapid cooling. While the synthetic gemstones show their origin by curved colour bands and by gas bubbles which are oriented along the curved layers, the striæ of glass is always at random, and sweeps in irregular curves in all directions in the material (*swirl striæ*). Likewise the gas bubbles have no special orientation; they are often arranged in groups, chains or "necklaces," which, under low magnification, sometimes appear similar to certain inclusions seen in real stones. Fissures and cracks may also appear, and small star-like markings may be seen which are due to incipient devitrification of the glass. Most sapphire-blue pastes show a red colour when they are viewed through the Chelsea Colour Filter, due to the coloration by cobalt. Pale blue pastes which owe their colour to copper and iron show green under the filter; these pastes imitate the blue aquamarine, blue zircon and the pale blue Ceylon sapphire. All green pastes show green and the amethyst colours show yellow to yellowish and brownish-red, similarly to the natural quartz amethyst. Most pastes (glass) glow under short-wave ultra-violet light and not under the long-wave ultra-violet rays. This effect may help in distinction between glass and some genuine stones.

The term "goldstone" is applied to a special type of glass which has bright spangles due to small triangular or hexagonal platelets of copper crystals. Usually brown in colour a blue variety of this stone is now marketed. Some glass is drawn out to give included gas bubbles a tubular shape and when these are fine a cat's-eye effect may be imparted to the stone.

OTHER MATERIALS

Some opaque gems and ornamental stones may be imitated in porcelain, a medium which is particularly suitable for imitations of turquoise. Little information is given in the literature as to the density of this material; however, the range of specific gravity may be said to lie between 2·1 to 2·5. The only other material which is used for gem simitation is the group of artificial resins popularly known as the "plastics." They have one thing in common, their extremely low specific gravity and hardness, which precludes any possibility of misidentification, except, perhaps, in the case of amber and jet. Amber has a lower S.G. than any plastic in general use, while jet chips when a knife-blade is applied to it contrary to the artificial resins, which peel. For guidance a table of the constants of the different types of the plastics is given.

	S.G.	R.I.
Cellulose nitrate ... ... (celluloid)	1·35 to 2·0 usually 1·37 to 1·43	1·495 to 1·520
Cellulose acetate ... ... (safety celluloid)	1·29 to 2·0 usually 1·29 to 1·35	1·49 to 1·51
Acrylate resins ... ... ("Perspex" and "Diakon")	1·18 to 1·19	1·495 to 1·500
Casein ... ... ("Lactoid," "Galalith," etc.)	1·315 to 1·39 usually 1·32 to 1·34	1·54 to 1·56
Phenol bakelites ... ... ("Bakelite," "Catalin," etc.)	1·2 to 1·7 clear types 1·25 to 1·35	1·56 to 1·67
Urea bakelites ... ... ("Beetle," etc.)	1·48 to 1·55	1·55 to 1·62
Polystyrene... ... ... ("Trolutol," "Distrene," etc.)	1·05	1·59 to 1·67

COMPOSITE STONES

THE simulation of gemstones by the use of two pieces of material joined together has been known from Roman times. These composite stones are generally described as *doublets* when the stones consist of two main pieces, and *triplets* when three pieces of material are joined together to form the stone. There are, however, some differences in the interpretation of these terms, for the *soudé-type* stones are called doublets in Europe but triplets in America.

There appear to be several reasons for the production of composite stones. It may well be that such a stone will provide a better wearing face; or may provide an apparently larger stone and/or of better colour and appearance. In the case of opal doublets the reason may be that, as the opal is often found only in thin seams, the backing may provide a support for the thin slice of opal. There are many different types of composite stones and the types better known will now be described.

True doublets, sometimes called *genuine doublets*, consist of two parts of the same type of genuine stone cemented together. They are rarely seen except in the case of opal, where a slice of colourful precious opal is cemented to an underlying piece of "potch" (opal not showing a play of colour).

Semi-genuine doublets are made by cementing a piece of genuine stone to a base of some other stone or even glass. The most important stone of this type is the *diamond doublet* in which the crown of the stone is a piece of real diamond. A new type of doublet is made with a crown of natural greenish-yellow sapphire backed with either synthetic blue sapphire or with synthetic ruby.

Schematic diagram of a true doublet.

Schematic drawing of a semi-genuine doublet (in this case a diamond doublet).

Schematic diagram of a soudé (quartz type) stone where the two pieces are made of rock crystal and the coloured layer along the girdle is gelatine (early type) or sintered glass (modern quartz type).

An unusual type of doublet. The stone is white or very pale pink topaz and the tip of the pavilion is made of natural blue sapphire. The effect was not very good, and the expected total blue coloration of the stone by total internal reflection did not occur.

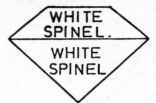

Schematic diagram of a spinel (soudé type) doublet.

Schematic diagram of a hollow doublet.

Schematic diagram of a garnet-topped doublet.

Schematic diagram of a false doublet.

Schematic diagram of a triplet.

FIG. 49.—**Types** of doublets.

False doublets consist of a crown of rock crystal or other colourless stone cemented to a base of glass. The only danger here is if the glass is citrine coloured or amethyst coloured with the crown of rock crystal, when a refractive index reading taken on the table facet will give the reading for either of these stones.

Hollow doublets are composite stones where a highly polished cavity is hollowed out of the piece forming the crown and this is filled with suitably coloured liquid. It is very rarely found.

Imitation doublets consist of two pieces of colourless glass, or one colourless and one coloured, which are cemented together—in the case of the two colourless pieces, with a layer of coloured cement between.

Garnet-topped doublets are commonly met with. They consist of a top of almandine garnet which is fused to a base of coloured glass. The garnet is usually so thin in relation to the depth of the stone as to have no great effect on the colour of the glass to which the colour of the stone is due. Such stones are made in all colours including colourless. A characteristic of these doublets is that the plane of joining is rarely across the plane of the girdle and is usually at an angle to it.

Soudé-type stones may be said to have three varieties. The earliest of these stones, made expressively to imitate the emerald, consisted of two pieces of rock crystal, often selected with natural inclusions, which were cemented together with a layer of green gelatine between them. They suffered from the fact that this green cement tended to go yellow with age and one was left with an imitation citrine instead of an emerald-coloured stone. Owing to the type of dyestuff used in the layer these stones showed a red residual colour through the colour filter. Later a better modification of this soudé stone was made; again with two pieces of rock crystal but with a layer, which, as far as is known, consists of sintered glass of suitable colour. These stones are usually green so as to imitate the emerald, and are usually called *soudé emeralds*, and, unlike the earlier type they show green through the colour filter. The third type of this stone consists, not of quartz top and bottom, but of two pieces of synthetic colourless spinel, with a coloured layer between, which can be almost any colour. Recently another variation of the soudé emerald has been produced using pale beryl in place of the rock crystal or synthetic white spinel for the crown and base.

Triplets are constructed of three pieces of stone, such as a rock crystal top and part base with a thick centre section of coloured glass between them. They are composite stones which are rarely met in practice. In recent years two different types of triplets have been produced. The first is the "Triplex opal," which is a conventional opal doublet embellished with a dome-shaped covering of transparent rock crystal. The other is a triplet made of three pieces of white jadeite cemented together with a green cement which gives to the stone the colour near the so-called "Imperial jade." What may also be termed a triplet is the *star-rose-quartz doublet*, which consists of a correctly oriented cabochon of star-rose-quartz cemented to a blue-coloured mirror and possibly completed with a third backing piece of some material, or in some cases the mirror is just sputtered on the back.

The detection of doublets is usually simple. One should first carefully examine the stone with a hand lens to see if there is a line of junction. In the garnet-topped doublets this may not be along the girdle but possibly half-way up the side facets of the crown; further, in these stones there will be seen the difference in relief of the garnet to the glass part of the stone. Soudé emeralds and other soudé stones can easily be detected by immersing the stone in water and observing the stone from the girdle direction, when the top and bottom of the stone will be seen to be colourless with a coloured line along the girdle. The spinel-type soudé stones may need immersion in a more highly refractive liquid than water for the effect to be easily seen. Apart from these modern soudées and garnet-topped doublets, immersion in oil should not be carried out unless imperative for the liquid may tend to dissolve the cement used.

Under the microscope garnet-topped doublets may show a bubble layer in one plane, the plane where the garnet is fused to the base, and there may be seen natural garnet inclusions in the garnet top of the stone. With diamond doublets, if the stone be viewed through the top at an angle with a light incident obliquely on the table, a reflection of the edge of the table facet on the cement layer will be seen. Loose garnet-topped doublets if laid table facet down on a white paper may show a red ring round the edge of the stone; and the jade triplet can often be detected, or if not queried, by the unusual absorption spectrum due to the dyestuff used in the green colouring. Examination by a microscope will with experience detect any composite stone.

A recent innovation, and a very deceptive one, is a doublet constructed by cementing a crown made of Australian natural greenish-yellow sapphire to a base of synthetic ruby or synthetic blue sapphire.

ARTIFICIALLY INDUCED COLOUR

ONE of the more interesting points in the study of gems is the facility
with which certain gemstones are able to change their colour when
influenced by heat and other radiations, and when crypto-crystalline
materials (such as the chalcedonies) are stained or dyed with different
colouring matter.

The most important method of colour change in gemstones, mainly
because it affects the diamond, is the colour change induced by
bombardment of the stone by high-speed atomic particles. As early
as 1904 W. Crookes found that diamonds placed adjacent to a radium
compound would turn to a green colour. The green colour induced
by such treatment is usually a rather blackish green, but much depends
upon the length of time the stone has been in contact with the radium
salt. Scientific investigation has shown that radium gives off radiations
of three different kinds, termed respectively α-, β- and γ-rays. Recent
research has shown that it is the α-particle bombardment which gives
rise to the colour change in diamonds. This colour change is permanent under ordinary conditions but may be destroyed by heating for
some hours at about 450° C. and also by the heating set up in the
process of repolishing. These radium-treated diamonds, like many
other substances so irradiated, themselves become radioactive and are
thus able to affect a photographic plate, a fluorescent screen or an
electroscope. It is by applying the test for radioactivity that these
radium-green diamonds may be differentiated from those rarely
found natural green diamonds.

Since the Second World War considerable extension of atomic
coloration of diamond has been carried out, not by radium, but by

more modern methods whereby high-speed atomic particles can attack and colour diamonds. There are three common methods of doing this and a brief survey of these methods, the effects they produce and something of the detection of this artificial coloration will be tabled.

Cyclotron bombardment. The particles used are usually protons or deuterons and the colour induced in the stones is like that induced by radium, that is, a rather dark green. Subsequent heat treatment turns the stones yellow or brown according to the depth of colour of the green treatment. Although intensely radioactive when they are removed from the cyclotron, this rapidly dies out and the stones cannot therefore be detected by the methods used for radium-treated diamonds. Some cyclotroned diamonds show peculiar "water-mark" areas which are indicative of the treatment, but it is with difficulty that the greened diamonds can be completely determined as having been treated. The yellows, on the other hand, usually show a characteristic absorption line at 5940A in the absorption spectrum.

Neutron bombardment. This is the colouring of diamonds by bombardment by neutrons from an atomic reactor (atomic pile, so the stones are sometimes known as pile treated diamonds). The coloration here is exactly the same as in the cyclotron treatment, but unlike the cyclotroned diamonds where the colour is only skin deep, the neutroned diamonds are coloured right through. These neutroned stones, like the cyclotroned stones, turn to brown or yellow on subsequent heat treatment after they have been greened. The methods of detection are the same as for the cyclotroned diamonds.

Electron bombardment. Electrons bombarding a diamond are thrown out by a different type of apparatus. This is called a Van de Graaff generator, and the colours induced in the diamonds vary from an aquamarine blue to a greenish blue. The coloration is skin deep and direct detection is not easy as the stones are not radioactive nor do they show any particular characteristics. All blue diamonds of natural origin are of the Type IIb and are electroconducting; this supplies a test as the electroned stones are found to be non-conducting.

Radium emanations tend to deepen the colour in many corundums and even, in the colourless stones, to induce it (in the collection of gemstones in the *Museum of Practical Geology* at South Kensington there is a white sapphire which has been turned brownish by the influence of radium. The colour has tended to fade during the years). Likewise atomic bombardment will induce colour, usually brownish, in other gemstones. X-rays will also alter the colour of some stones, particularly the Ceylon yellow sapphire, pale stones being altered to a strong "topaz" colour; and the lilac pink kunzite to a green. In all cases the colour is not permanent and goes off after a time. Citrines and amethysts which have had their colour driven off by the application of heat (to be mentioned later in the text) are reported to have the colour restored when subsequently treated by radium emanations. This restored colour may not be the tint the stone had before the heat treatment. Radio-active isotopes have also been used to artificially colour gemstones.

Many different species of gemstones are altered in colour when they undergo heating. These colour changes are in general permanent and have a great commercial significance. The application of heat to coloured corundum and quartz has the effect of weakening the colour. Purple sapphires are heat-treated to produce a rose red or pink colour, while amethyst, which turns colourless under great heat, with a moderate temperature may turn to a deep orange, the so-called "Spanish topaz," or to a lighter yellow or citrine colour. Some amethysts turn to a green colour on heating and are then sold under the name "Prasiolite." Brown tourmaline loses its colour by heat, producing the colourless variety—achroite. The tourmalines from Klein Spitzkopje in South-west Africa, of a dark blue-green colour, lighten, when heated to about 650° C., to a light green colour tinged with blue, which at times resembles the emerald. Greenish beryl, when heated, changes its colour to a beautiful blue. Some kunzite which often has an unpleasant yellowish tinge when found, may have this removed by judicious heating. The fine sapphire blue zoisites (tanzanites) owe their fine colour to heat treatment.

Probably the classic instances of thermal colour change are those of topaz and zircon, both species of which have an exceptional interest in modern gem trade. Brownish and yellow topaz from Ouro Preto, Brazil, when heated to 500° to 600° C., lose their colour, but on slowly cooling assume an attractive shade of pink which permanently remains. Should the heat be too great, the stone remains colourless and at too low a temperature the colour assumed is a salmon pink. The process is termed *pinking*, and the stones are known as "pinked," "fired," or "burnt" topaz. The brown zircons from Indo-China supply the material for the beautiful zircons now so popular and whose colour has been obtained by heat treatment. These brown zircons when heated in a reducing atmosphere, such as in a crucible packed with wood charcoal, which gives an atmosphere of carbon monoxide, usually turn a shade of blue. Stones of this hue are known under the name of Starlight or Starlite; the colour, however, is often fugitive. If the brown stones are heated in an oxidising atmosphere (in air) the colour assumed is golden yellow or colourless. The colourless stones are highly refractive and dispersive, and give a good simulation of diamond when they are viewed in a half light. These colourless stones are sometimes known as "Matura diamond."

Materials of a crypto-crystalline nature, and thereby somewhat porous, are capable of being stained or dyed to various colours. This is particularly so in the case of chalcedony and agates. The so-called "black onyx" is produced by boiling chalcedony in a solution of sugar and water followed by treatment with sulphuric acid. The action is as follows: During the first boiling the sugar penetrates into the interstices of the chalcedony and is deposited. Sugar has the chemical formula of $C_{12}H_{22}O_{11}$. $H_{22}O_{11}$ is eleven times H_2O (or water) and in the final treatment, with sulphuric acid, the acid, with its great affinity for water, abstracts the $H_{22}O_{11}$, leaving C_{12}, which is carbon, and in the form of soot, in the interstices and thus producing the black colour. Ferrous sulphate solution gives a blue colour to a chalcedony which has previously been soaked in potassium ferrocyanide, while if the stone is soaked in ferrous sulphate and then heated ferric oxide is left in the interstices which produces a red colour. Treatment with chromium and nickel gives green colours and with hydrochloric acid a yellow colour is produced. Various other shades are produced by the use of aniline dyes, but the colours are apt to be fugitive. Jasper, the impure quartz, is stained to produce *Swiss or German Lapis* and *Swiss jade*. Some opal matrix from Andamooka in South Australia is stained black by a similar method to the staining of black onyx and is then sold as "treated black opal." Some cabochons of white jadeite have been stained to an "Imperial Jade" colour, but the effect is not permanent. Alabaster and amber are two other materials to which the art of staining has been actively applied. Bad coloured turquoise has had the colour enhanced by staining, and the white mineral *howlite* has been stained to a good turquoise blue colour. Rock crystal has been heated till cracks are apparent and then placed in coloured solutions or inks, which enter the cracks and give the stone a coloured appearance. Such stones are called "Firestones." Another type of staining, if it can be so called, is used for the purposes of deceit. "Off"-coloured diamonds are painted on the back facets with aniline blue, which appears to correct to some degree the yellowish colour and make the stone whiter in appearance and more valuable. The effect lasts only for a short time. Washing in spirit will usually remove the colour and unmask the fake, though recently some faked stones needed boiling in acid for removal of the colour. If the facet edges and the ground edge of the girdle are examined with a lens some of the blue colour will show up. In America a similar type of back facet coloration is carried out by a "vacuum sputtering" technique. This is more effective and is with some difficulty identified. Poor coloured rubies, sapphires, emeralds, topazes and amethysts are often found with the back facets painted, and the Mexican water opal is sometimes found with the back painted black. The latter artificial coloration, one is told, is not fraudulent.

Recently beryl, topaz and quartz, and possibly diamond, have been improved or altered in colour by bombardment with gamma rays from radio-active isotopes.

STYLES OF CUTTING

IT has already been learned that when gemstones are found in nature they may have distinctive forms with plane and often lustrous faces. These faces and edges may suffer attrition during the course of the countless years since their original formation, and may be completely rubbed away, leaving a simple rolled pebble. Even in the most perfect crystal there is little likelihood of the gem showing the beauty and symmetry which is brought out by the art of the precious stone cutter or lapidary, as he is more correctly called, although it may be pointed out that the man who cuts diamonds prefers not to be so named, but is simply known as the diamond cutter, the lapidary being a worker whose job is principally the cutting of fine gems from the species which supply precious, rare and ornamental stones.

There is one main difference between the fashioning of diamonds and that of other stones. Diamonds can only be cut and polished by their own powder, and the cutting and polishing is carried out on a rotating lap in one operation. In fact, the polishing of diamond is simply a fine grinding, that is the "hills and dales" are gradually rubbed down level. It is remarkable that with the other gemstones the final process of polishing is not a fine grinding but a flowing of the surface layer of atoms which produces an amorphous layer, the Beilby layer, which either remains amorphous or re-crystallizes.

In the cutting and polishing of other stones, two separate processes are carried out, again on rotating laps. The facets are cut by the use of hard abrasives to obtain the outline and shape of the finished stone. This leaves the faces with a ground-glass effect. Each of these facets is now polished on another lap using various soft polishing materials, such as rotten-stone, tripoli powder, etc., in order to produce the mirror-like surfaces seen on a cut stone.

So that the maximum beauty of a stone may be apparent, certain definite shapes and angular measurements, particularly in the case of diamond, are necessary. In dichroic stones, such as ruby, sapphire, emerald, tourmaline, etc., care has to be taken that the table facet is placed in the correct direction to ensure the best colour. All this has of necessity produced a series of "styles" of cutting most suitable for each particular type of stone. These styles will now be briefly described.

CABOCHON CUTS

The simplest cut for a stone. Consists of a curved (or domed) upper surface, which may be low, medium or steep, with a base of less curvature (double cabochon), or flat, or the base may be hollowed, out. The outline of cabochon cuts may be circular, oval or elliptical or even pear-shaped. This style is most suitable for translucent and opaque stones, and such stones which have particular optical effects, such as cat's-eyes and star-stones; it is also used for opal and for dark-coloured garnets, when the cabochon cut with a hollow base is used in order to lighten the stone. Such garnets may then be known as *carbuncles*.

ROSE CUT

Generally used for cleavage fragments of diamond, and for the pyrope garnet used in Victorian jewellery. The rose cut consists of a series of triangular facets of equal size rising from the flat base and terminating in a point at the apex. A double rose may be explained as being two roses base to base. Very small diamonds which have been polished with three or four triangular facets are called "chips" and are not strictly the rose cut, although often so-called *roses* by jewellers.

BRILLIANT CUT

This is the perfection cut for diamond; the cut which allows the greatest amount of brilliancy and "fire" to be seen. There are fifty-eight facets in the standard brilliant cut, thirty-three above the girdle and twenty-five below. For diamonds, and other colourless stones, it

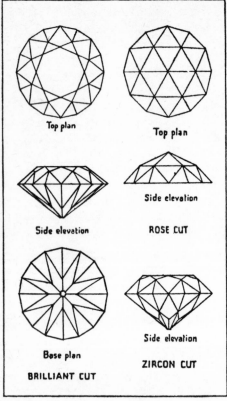

FIG. 50.—Cuts of stones.

is important to ensure that the greater proportion of light falling on the front of the stone should strike the rear facets at angles greater than the critical angle for the mineral concerned, and thus be totally reflected back to the eye of the observer. Then the full brilliancy of the stone is seen and the effect of "fire" given full play. For diamond the angle between the crown facets and the girdle must be between 35° and 37°, and similarly that between the girdle and the pavilions must be 41°. In an ideal stone, the depth of the crown should be one-third the total depth of the stone. In the modern "sawn" stone the height of the crown is less than that postulated as necessary for perfection, but this seems to have little detrimental effect on the brilliancy.

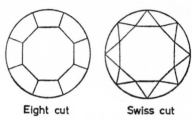

Eight cut   **Swiss cut**

FIG. 51.—The Swiss and Eight cuts.

In the standard round brilliant there is the large central eight-sided *table* facet which is surrounded by eight triangular *star* facets. There are eight main facets called *bezels*, four of which are known as *quoins* and four as *templets*. These latter terms are the diamond cutters terms and as the eight facets are alike cannot be determined after cutting. To complete the *crown* or top of the stone there are sixteen triangular facets bordering the *girdle* or setting edge of the stone. These facets are variously called *skill*, *cross* or *break* facets, or *halves*. On the bottom part of the stone, below the girdle, are a similar set of sixteen *skill* facets, eight *pavilion* facets and a small facet at the point called the *culet* which is parallel to the table facet. In modern practice this may not be put on.

If the outline of the stone is other than round, or if the stone be exceptionally large, more facets may be put on, but generally the symmetry remains the same. The *marquise* is a boat-shaped modification of the brilliant-cut, while the *pendeloque* is a drop-shaped form. Small diamonds are now cut with less number of facets than used in

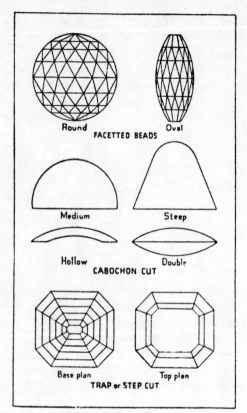

FIG. 52.—Cuts of stones.

the standard brilliant. These are respectively the "Swiss-cut" and the "Eight-cut." Fig. 51 will show the design of such stones. The *zircon-cut* is similar to the brilliant but eight extra facets are added between the pavilions and the culet in order to assist in the reflection of light which might pass out in this region. It is a style which has been used extensively for zircon. The "Profile cut," earlier known as the "Princess-cut," consists of thin tabular stones cut with parallel facets on the back of the stone.

STEP, TRAP OR EMERALD CUT

This cut, which may be arranged on an outline of a square with cut corners, square, oblong, triangular, long bag-shaped (baguette) and various fancy outlines, has a table facet and a series of rectangular facets arranged parallel to the girdle both on the crown and base. This is the

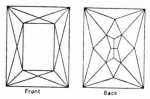

FIG. 53.—The scissors cut or cross cut

cut most used for emerald and, in modern practice, for diamond, although its use precludes the full amount of fire being brought out.

A modification of the trap cut consists of the long rectangular facets on the side of the crown being divided into four triangular facets. This is called the "scissors" or "cross" cut.

MIXED CUT

This cut, which is used for various coloured stones, consists of a crown cut in the brilliant style and with the base step cut.

A *briolette* is a drop-shaped stone having its entire surface cut with triangular facets. *Seal cut* is the name applied to a stone, usually trap cut, with a wide table. A *cameo* is a stone with a raised carved image; if the carving is engraved into the stone, as for the purposes of a seal, the stone is termed an *intaglio*. A *curvette* is a cameo engraved so that the design has a hollowed background with the edge of the stone raised as much as the central design.

There are many other variations of cuts to which names have been given, but they are, or can be, described as variations of the types mentioned above. The term "fancy cut" may be safely used to describe them. The term *calibre*, which means "measured," is properly used for stones "cut to measure" for incorporation into a special jewellery design. However, this term is commonly used for small step-cut stones.

Gemstones are weighed in *carats*, a weight now internationally

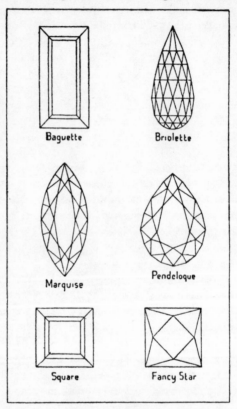

FIG. 54.—Cuts of stones.

recognized as being one-fifth of a gram (1 carat = 0·2 gram = 200 milligram), and in commercial practice the weighing is not carried beyond the second place of decimal. Some ornamental stones are weighed in grams, and some stones, particularly the synthetic corundums and spinels, and some quartz, are sold by their measurement in millimetres. *Mélée* is the term used for small diamonds of mixed sizes below about $\frac{1}{4}$ carat; and *Mélange* is the corresponding term for a mixture of larger sizes.

It may be well to conclude this lesson with some remarks on the methods and the machinery used in the cutting of diamond and other gemstones. Until the present century the polishing process was thought to be merely one of superfine abrasion; the uneven surface being ground flat and then subjected to finer and finer grinding until any scratches thereon were too small to be visible. Early in this century G. T. Beilby found that on polishing there is usually an actual flow of the solid surface with a formation of a liquid-like layer which is called the *Beilby layer*. This lies like a coat of varnish over the underlying scratches which are hidden not smoothed away, as etching with acid reveals them again. It is now known that the Beilby layer can take one of four types. They are as follows:

1. The melting point of the substance being too high for the necessary local fusion the polishing is simply a fine abrasion. This is the case with diamond and is the answer to the difference in the methods used in cutting this gemstone.
2. A Beilby layer is formed but this immediately recrystallizes in conformity with the underlying crystal structure. This occurs particularly with corundum and quartz.
3. The Beilby layer remains amorphous except when parallel to important crystal planes, or on long heating. Calcite and kyanite are examples of stones in which this occurs.
4. Here the Beilby layer is amorphous and remains so on all surfaces, as in the case of spinel and zircon which are typical examples of this type of Beilby layer.

The Beilby layer is much too thin to affect the refractive index reading by a refractometer and the shadow edge so obtained is that of the underlying solid.

The cutting of a diamond from a rough crystal is carried out in a number of stages. After a preliminary inspection the stone is marked with ink if it has to be reduced in size by cleaving or sawing. *Cleaving*, by taking advantage of the directions of weakness called cleavage, is only carried out on stones of large size, or those which are mis-shapen or badly flawed. A notch is ground with another diamond along the ink-marked line. A heavy bladed "knife" is then placed in the notch and held in line with the cleavage direction and the blade then given a sharp blow with a short iron bar. The stone then splits across.

It is now more common practice to "saw" the stone, particularly if it be a well-formed octahedral crystal. The stone is fixed in a clamp and allowed to rest by gravity on the "saw," the direction it is to be sawn first having been marked out by ink. The "saw" itself is a thin phosphor-bronze disc about 2 inches in radius and allowed to rotate at about 5,000 to 6,000 revolutions per minute. The edge of the disc is spread so as to be thicker at the cutting edge in order to prevent the saw jamming in the cut, and this edge is impregnated with diamond dust and olive oil from a roller which forces the diamond powder into the edge of the "saw." The saw cut is always started from a corner of the crystal, a notch being ground first in order to guide the saw.

The sawn or cleaved stone is now ground into the form of a truncated double cone by the process known as *bruting* or *grinding*; it is also called "cutting." Previously carried out by hand by rubbing two stones, each of which is cemented into a holder, one against the other, the method is now made less laborious by mounting one stone in the headstock of a lathe and grinding another, held in a stick, against it. The speed of the lathe is about 1,000 revolutions per minute and the diamond selected for the lathe chuck is one having worn edges.

The ground stone is now passed to the *cross worker* who cuts the table facet and the four main facets (the bezels), and the opposite pavilion facets on the base of the stone, and also the culet if one is put on. To do this he mounts the stone in a special holder called a solder dop, which consists of a copper cup filled with solder and has a strong copper stem. Modern practice is to now use a mechanical dop in which the stone is held in claws. The stem (tail) of the dop is held in a clamp which forms the other two legs of a tripod. This clamp is called a *tang* and the third leg is formed by the dop itself containing the diamond which rests on a rapidly rotating horizontal cast-iron disc, known as the lap or *scaife*. The scaife is about 12 inches across and about $\frac{1}{2}$ inch thick and rotates absolutely evenly at about 2,500 revolutions per minute. The stone is pressed into contact with the scaife, which is charged with diamond dust and oil, by weights placed on the bridge of the tang; a stop is placed on the cutting bench, or *mill* as it is called, to prevent the tang moving under the influence of the movement of the scaife. Three or four dops are placed on the scaife simultaneously, but at different distances from the centre, in order to avoid undue grooving of the scaife.

The polishing of a diamond can only proceed properly across the *grain*, which is the direction of the cleavage traces where they meet the surface. The cutter, therefore, first examines the stone to determine the "point" which in turn tells him which way the grain will run. A "four-point" stone is one with the table facet parallel to a cube face with the grain parallel to its edges. A "sawn" stone is usually a four-point stone. A "three-point" stone has the table facet parallel to the octahedral face with the grain forming an equilateral triangle, and a "two-point" stone is one with the table facet parallel to the face of the dodecahedron, and in this case there is only one grain direction. The diamond cutter usually finds by trial and error the optimum position.

After the stone has had the four top and four bottom main facets and the table put on by the cross worker, it is returned to the bruter to *square up*, the stone is passed to the *finisher*, more often called the *brillianteerder*, who polishes on the quoins and the other facets of the crown and pavilion. The girdle is usually left unpolished and may even show traces of the crystal faces. Some firms polish the girdles either circularly or with rectangular facets.

Diamond, as it has no Beilby layer, is cut and polished in one operation, but with the stones of other species there must be two distinct operations—that of cutting the stones to form, which leaves the facets with a ground–glass finish, and then polishing these facets to a mirror-like surface. A rough piece of gem material is first sawn to a shape suitable for cutting, by the use of a vertical diamond or carborundum charged disc. Although this is very like the sawing of diamond, in the case of these stones the material is held in the hand while being sawn. The rough piece is then taken to the *cutter* who, using a cast-iron, copper or gunmetal horizontal lap, grinds on the facets Diamond dust, carborundum or emery is used as the abrasive, and the angles of the facets are to some extent controlled by the angle made between the *gemstick*, into which the stone is cemented, and the *gem peg*, or *amb peg*, which is a vertical post drilled with a number of holes into which the end of the gem stick is inserted. The stone is then thoroughly cleaned so that no abrasive is left on the surface and then transferred to another bench for the *polisher* to polish the already ground-on facets. This is carried out on copper, pewter or wooden laps, which are often covered by leather or cloth, with polishing compounds, such as rouge, rotten-stone, cerium or chromium oxides as the polishing powder. The use of mechanical stone holders has to some extent simplified the work of gem cutting but the best work is still carried out by hand.

The engraving of cameos and intaglios is carried out by the use of small burrs fitted into a drill chuck on a drill head or flexible drive. Holes may be drilled by needles charged with diamond powder or other abrasive, or by similarly charged tube drills.

"Tumbled" gemstones are produced by grinding rough gem material to an irregular shape in a rotating "churn" using a grinding powder; and then similarly polishing the stones in another "churn" or drum using this time a polishing powder.

THE PEARL

THE earlier instalments of this series gave account of gems and imitations which were the products of the mineral constituents of the earth, or, in the case of the counterfeits, the fruits of the work of the world's chemists and technologists. However, there is one group of gems which have as their genesis the living creature or the growing plant, that is, their origin is organic and not mineral.

Chief among this group of gems is that prized possession, the pearl, that gem of Queens which from remote days has always been known as "The Queen of Gems." Embellished with legend and fact, pearl, despite its lack of durability, has survived all endeavours to relegate its importance below that of its consort—diamond.

What is pearl, and how is it formed? These are the first and essential questions to consider, for beyond the common knowledge that pearls are found in oysters, little other information is imparted to the ordinary layman. Practically all shellfish, and in particular all those which are grouped in the zoological phylum mollusca, have the power to produce the substances which together produce pearls and mother-of-pearl, but it is only in certain types that pearls as we know them as gems are found.

The "oyster" (the animal is not strictly an oyster, at least not of the same zoological family as are the succulent morsels so well known to the gourmet) has the power to secrete crystalline carbonate of lime and an organic substance known under the name of conchiolin in order to produce the hard covering, or shell, which serves as the protection to the soft body of the animal, and it is this secretion which will, in certain abnormal conditions, where damage or injury causes irritation to the animal, produce the various types of pearls. There are two main types of pearls: the *cyst* pearls, which are spherical or pear-shaped pearls found inside the body of the animal and constituting the finest and most valuable type of gem; and *blister* pearls, which are those found attached to the inside of the shell, and are produced by a piece of irritant lying between the inside surface of the shell and the outside of the animal, which has been covered over by the pearly secretion. Other names sometimes applied to pearls are as follows: *Button* or *Bouton* pearls are cyst pearls which have rounded tops and flat bases, while *Drops* or *Pear-eyes* are, as their name implies, pear-shaped, and are always cyst pearls. *Baroque* or *Barrok* pearls are irregularly shaped pearls which may be either cyst or blister in formation. *Seed-pearls* is the name applied to very small pearls. *Fresh-water pearls* or *mussel-pearls* are pearls found in mussels of the family *Unionidæ*, which live in inland waters and rivers. A full list of the various types of pearl oyster and mussel and other shellfish which produce pearls will be tabled later.

Before proceeding further, it may be as well to give some indication of the general structure of the pearl-forming mollusc. One of the more rudimentary forms of animal life, the mollusc consists of a soft visceral mass, having no head, but obtaining its sustenance through gills. The rest of the animal consists of a *foot* and a bundle of horny threads, termed the *byssus*, whereby the animal attaches itself to the rocky sea bottom. Lastly, but of utmost importance in the production of pearl and mother-of-pearl, is the *mantle*, a double flap which completely encloses the animal, and consists, at least on its outer surface, of epithelial cells which are capable of secreting the various constituents which go to the making of pearl and mother-of-pearl. The mantle has the property of being able to secrete the various components in a given order; thus, in the secretion of the material for the shell, the cells at the outer edge of the flaps secrete a brownish, organic substance which approximates to the formula $C_{30}H_{48}N_2O_{11}$ and which is termed *conchiolin*. Nearer the centre of the mantle, the cells secrete carbonate of lime (calcium carbonate $= CaCO_3$) in a form of prismatic crystals minute in size, while the secretion from the cells at the centre of the mantle is also carbonate of lime; the crystals are in the form of flakes, and arrange themselves in an overlapping arrangement reminiscent of roofing tiles. This layer produces the beautiful iridescent *nacreous* surface so well known in mother-of-pearl. Hence, by this process, the shell of the animal is built up of an external layer of brown conchiolin (the *periostracum*), a layer of variable thickness of carbonate of lime in the form of prismatic crystals of calcite, and, finally, an inside smooth layer, known as the *nacreous layer*, which consists of platy crystals of carbonate of lime in the aragonite modification. This forms a smooth surface for the body of the animal to rest upon.

The above description is that of the formation of a pearl shell; in the case of pearls, however, there is generally no trace of the prismatic (calcite) layer and the whole of the pearl consists of nacre, the minute crystallites of aragonite forming in a previously deposited framework of conchiolin. Further, these small crystals are deposited in layers, producing the concentric layers like that of an onion, and have their vertical axes at right angles to the surface of these layers. Thus, the structure of a pearl is both concentric and radial, and it is upon this that the methods of testing pearls depend to a great extent.

The beautiful iridescent lustre of mother-of-pearl and pearls is due to a combination of two optical phenomena, and the combined effect is termed the *orient*. It is due to the combined effect of interference of light at thin films (as in the case of opal), and diffraction of light from the fine lines, or edges, produced by the overlapping of the flakes of the nacreous layer.

So much for the shell and mother-of-pearl, a natural arrangement to protect the animal. What, then, of pearls in the scheme of things? It should be noted when a shell is examined that the outside is rough while the inside is smooth, smooth, as before pointed out, to rest against the outer envelope of the animal; however, should a sharp piece of grit, such as a grain of sand, a piece of broken shell, or even the intrusion of a shell-boring animal get between the shell and the mantle, it is logical to suppose that the animal would attempt to ease the irritation caused. This is precisely what it does, and it does so by secreting nacre over the obstruction, which is cemented to the shell and finished off by layers of smooth nacre. The bump, or bulge, produced on the shell may be removed and used as a jewel, and is then known as a blister pearl. This pearl is caused through an injury or protection against injury to the animal; in fact, all pearls are due to injury or disease, hence are an abnormal condition.

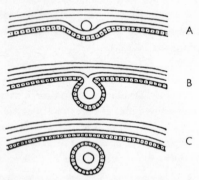

Fig. 55.—Diagrammatic picture of the formation of a "cyst" pearl. A, the irritant forms a dent in the "mantle." B, the "mantle" forms a pouch which contains the irritant. C, the pouch separates from the "mantle" forming a "cyst" in the body of the animal. This pouch is the "pearl sac" and contains the irritant.

In certain conditions, the obstruction, or irritant, is not cemented to the shell, and a second method is adopted by the animal to immobilize the irritation. This method involves the formation of a pearl inside the body of the animal, and produces the so-called *cyst* pearl. The irritant, usually a trematode or cestode worm, gradually, and in successive stages, forms a dent in the mantle, fig. *55a*, a bag-shaped pouch, fig. *55b*, which eventually joins together at the neck, producing a hollow sphere, lined with epithelial cells quite separate from the mantle of which it was originally a part, fig. *55c*. This sphere of cells is termed the *pearl sac*. The wound in the mantle coalesces and leaves the pearl sac within the animal as a tumour or cyst. The cells lining the wall of the cyst are still living, and go on secreting nacre over the irritant, thus building up the pearl. Given good position within the animal, the pearl is normally round in shape, but if in an unfavourable position may produce bizarre shapes (baroque pearls) or drops or boutons.

The percentage chemical composition of pearl is about 86 per cent carbonate of lime, 12 per cent conchiolin and 2 per cent water, and the structure is made up of concentric shells. The density of pearl lies within the range 2·60 to 2·78; however, each fishery usually conforms to a narrower range of density. These closer figures are in the table given later. The hardness of pearl is about $3\frac{1}{2}$ to 4.

The chief pearl fisheries are as follows: in the Persian Gulf, off the coast of Arabia; the Gulf of Manaar, off the north-west coast of Ceylon; off the north-west coast of Australia; the Mergui Archipelago, off the coast of southern Burma; the Sulu Sea; around New Guinea and Borneo; certain Pacific islands, including Tahiti; the Gulf of Mexico and off the coast of Venezuela and the Gulf of California in the New World. Fresh-water pearls are found in rivers of England, Scotland and Wales, and in the rivers of North America.

Black pearls are obtained from the Gulf of Mexico and, to a limited extent, from certain Pacific islands; the colour is thought to be caused by the nature of the water. Blue pearls are due to a large kernel of conchiolin, and are lead-grey in colour rather than blue. Yellow pearls are obtained from Shark Bay, Western Australia. Pink pearls are obtained from a univalve mollusc, the great conch, fished off the coast of Florida and the West Indies. All pink conch pearls are characterized by the lack of nacreous coating, by their high specific gravity = 2·85, and by the typical "flame-like" markings seen on their surface.

Other molluscs which sometimes produce pearls are the giant clam (*Tridacna gigas*), the wing-shell (*Pinna*), the sea mussels (*Mytilidæ*), and the following mussels—the niggerhead (*Quadrula ebena*), the bullhead (*Pleurobema*), the butterfly (*Plagiola securis*), the buckhorn

TABLE

Pearl Composition.

Carbonate of Lime (aragonite)	S.G. = 2·94
Conchiolin.	S.G. = 1·34
Water	S.G. = 1·00

Locality	Mollusc.	Colour of Pearl.	Range of S.G.
Persian Gulf.	Pinctada Vulgaris.	Creamy-white.	2·68 to 2·74
Gulf of Manaar.	Pinctada Vulgaris.	Pale cream-white.	2·68 to 2·74
North coast of Australia.	Pinctada margaritifera.	Silver-white.	2·68 to 2·78
North-west coast of Australia.	Pinctada maxima.	Silver-white.	2·67 to 2·78
Shark Bay, W. Australia.	Pinctada carcharium.	Yellow.	
Venezuela.	Pinctada radiata.	White.	2·65 to 2·75
Japan (natural).	Pinctada martensi.	White, with greenish tinge.	2·66 to 2·76
Florida, and Gulf of California.	Strombus gigas (the great conch).	Pink.	2·85
	Haliotidæ (the abalone).	Greens, yel-lows, blues, etc.	
Gulf of Mexico.		Black.	2·61 to 2·69
Freshwater pearls. North America.	Unio.	White.	2·66 to over 2·78
Europe.	Unio margaritifera.	White.	
Cultured pearls. Japan.	Pinctada martensi.	White.	2·72 to 2·78

(*Tritigonia verrucosa*) and some others. An oval section of the rounded whorl of the nautilus, backed with cement, resembles a blister pearl, and is called *coque de perle*.

Owing to the organic constituent, pearls, unlike the gems cut from crystals, are not so durable, being much softer. Moreover, each crystallite of carbonate of lime is kept in its place by a cementing of the organic conchiolin, and this constituent may deteriorate during the course of years, turn dark, show cracks, and subsequently crumble away.

CULTIVATION OF PEARL

It has been explained that if a foreign body gets between the shell and the body of an oyster or mussel the animal takes steps to cover the intruder with nacre, and thus produces a blister pearl. Knowing little of the science of the pearl-bearing molluscs, the Chinese, in the thirteenth century, found that if they inserted an object between the shell and the animal, it subsequently became coated with pearly nacre. Even to this day, metal figures of Buddha are so treated. During the later half of the nineteenth century, the Japanese advanced on the method. They cemented mother-of-pearl pellets to the inner side of the shell of the mollusc. After the animal had been returned to the sea for some years and then again fished up, it was found that the pellet had been covered over the exposed surface with nacre. The bead was then broken away from the shell and the broken surface ground flat. A piece of mother-of-pearl was then pegged on to the ground base and finished by grinding to a symmetrical shape to produce the whole sphere. The so-called *mabe pearls* are cultured blister pearls which have been grown on the shell over a soft talc-like bead. This original bead is removed; the inside of the hollow dome of nacre is cleaned, and often tinted, and then a smaller bead is cemented into the cavity with white cement. The whole is then backed with a base of mother-of-pearl (fig. 56). If these *half-cultured pearls* are mounted in a setting with a closed back, the raw mother-of-pearl base is not seen, but if they are unset, the deceptive nature is at once apparent.

It was not until 1921, after some seven or more years experimental work by the Japanese scientists led by Mikimoto, that the cultured pearl as we know it today, the *whole-cultured pearl*, appeared. The method employed to produce these pearls, highly technical in nature, has of late years been brought to a mass-production basis. Briefly, the process is as follows: An oyster fished at maturity, that is about three years old, has inserted into its body, through an incision made with a scalpel, due care being taken that the wound is aseptic, a mother-of-pearl bead contained in a sac of epithelial cells formed from the centre of the mantle cut from another mature oyster, which is killed by the operation. This sac, containing the mother-of-pearl, is closed by a

FIG. 56.—Cultured blister pearls. A, Ordinary type. B, Mabe type.

ligature, and the wound in the second, and living, oyster is antiseptically treated. The oyster is then returned to the sea for a period of years, being kept in wire cages during the time. On being fished up after this period of time, the bead is found to have been coated with a nacreous layer, the bag of epithelial cells having carried out the work of secreting the nacre in exactly the same way as that carried out by the pearl sac in the case of an oyster producing a natural pearl. The *all lapped* process of using a *sac* of mantle was found to be wasteful of oysters, so nowadays only a small dice of mantle about 2 mm. square is inserted into the oyster and this is followed by the bead. This small dice of epithelial tissue grows round the bead forming the essential *pearl sac*.

Let us now consider the difference between this cultured pearl, which from external examination appears much the same as the real pearl, and the pearl produced by an accident of nature. The natural pearl, when sliced through, appears to be a series of concentric shells with, or without, a distinguishable nucleus. On the other hand, a section of a cultured pearl shows the parallel banded structure of the mother-of-pearl bead surrounded by a thin series of layers concentrically arranged around the bead.

At first placed upon the market as pearls from a new fishery, their true nature was not at once discovered; not until a pearl was broken and the mother-of-pearl bead discovered, was the character of this counterfeit made known. Then came the necessity of finding a method whereby these pearls could be distinguished from the natural pearl. It is obvious that one could not break open every pearl to find out whether it had a core or not. Probably the first attempt to find a solution was to use the valuable penetrating power of X-radiations to see if the core would show up as a darker shadow, as the bones of a hand show as a dark shadow through the much more easily penetrated flesh. Owing to technical difficulties at the time the technique was not pursued. Cultured pearls, when viewed in the dark whilst they were irradiated by a beam of invisible ultra-violet light, were found to fluoresce with a greenish tint as against the sky-blue fluorescence of natural pearls. Unfortunately, again a snag destroyed the value of this test when it was found that later samples of cultured pearls gave a similar fluorescence to natural pearls.

Nearly all pearls are drilled through in order that they may be strung as necklets, and this string canal provides a means whereby the centre of the pearl may be examined. A special form of microscope will give much indication as to whether there is a bead centre present, but this method, much used by the German gemmologists, does not provide conclusive evidence in all cases. Probably the most satisfactory means of detecting cultured pearls which have been drilled is by the *endoscope*, a French invention. The apparatus consists of a strong source of light which is directed down a narrow platinum tube fitted with two mirrors at angles of 45° in opposite senses at its end. The pearl is threaded along the needle until the mirrors are central when the light passing upwards from the first mirror is, if the pearl be natural, reflected along the adjacent concentric layer to be reflected from the second mirror and out along the string canal. This is viewed by a low-power microscope and when the pearl is moved along the needle a flash is seen in the microscope eyepiece when the pearl is central on the needle (fig. 57). Should the pearl be cultured, the reflected beam will proceed up and along the parallel layers of the mother-of-pearl bead, and will be seen as a streaky effect on the outside of the pearl. No flash of light is seen in the microscope eyepiece when a cultured pearl is moved along the needle (fig. 57). This instrument requires some practice in operation, but in the hands of an experienced worker, something like 200 pearls an hour can be tested.

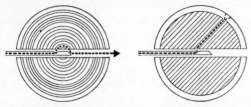

FIG. 57.—Schematic diagram of the action of the endoscope.

Should the pearl not be drilled, the endoscopic method is not available, and another method must be utilized. Earlier in the article it was mentioned that the use of X-radiations was not at first found practicable if used in the same way as in medical diagnosis, *i.e.* shadow or so-called skiagrams, though recent research by Dr. A. E. Alexander has shown that successful results can be obtained. We have, then, to consider another way in which the radiations could be of use. Fluorescence generated by X-rays has some value, and earlier had been used with partial success. The method in use at the present day depends on the experimental work of scientists investigating the nature of X-rays. In 1912, Max von Laue instigated practical experiments based on the theory that X-rays were electro-magnetic radiations with a much shorter wave-length than light, and that if a structure could be found in which regular divisions were close enough together, then if the rays were as suggested, they could be diffracted by such a structure, as are light waves by a finely ruled glass diffraction grating. Using a crystal of copper sulphate, he found that this acted towards X-rays as a three-dimensional grating, thus proving the theory of the connection between the light rays and X-rays. Max von Laue also discovered that the pattern of reflected spots gave information of the atomic arrangement, thus leading to the science of X-ray crystal analysis.

It has been found that if a lauegram, that is the photograph of the spots diffracted from the crystal, is taken across the short axes of a bundle of aragonite crystals, the pattern shows four heavy spots, while if taken in the direction of the long axes, the design is hexagonal, with six spots. Now if a narrow beam of X-rays is passed through the centre of a real pearl, it is obvious that, owing to the radial nature of the small crystals, the beam must pass along the long axes of the crystals, and, hence, that a pattern will show the six-spot hexagon. If, however, a cultured pearl is so examined, there is only one direction in which the beam will pass along the long axes, thus producing a six-spot figure; all other directions will cut across the short axes of the crystals and, hence, show four-spot figures. In testing a pearl, should the first picture show a six-spot figure, the pearl must be rotated through a right angle, and a further photo taken. If this also shows a six-spot photo, the pearl is natural; if a four-spot figure is shown, the pearl is cultured. In general, one obtains the four-spot diagram at once with a cultured pearl, and no further testing is needed (fig. 58).

The earlier failure to obtain a satisfactory X-ray direct picture of pearls has now been mostly overcome. This is obtained by the use of fine-grain film which allows the finer structures of the pearls to be seen; and by special techniques, such as immersing the pearls in liquid having a similar X-ray density to the pearls, or by holding them in a wax such as "Plasticene." Control of the development is also necessary. The method will not always give a 100 per cent answer, but a great deal can be done in far less time than by the use of the lauegram method or even by endoscope if cultured pearls are the problem.

Recent careful determinations of the specific gravity of natural and cultured pearls, by B. W. Anderson and C. J. Payne, have shown that the cultured pearl has a relatively high specific gravity coupled to a more restricted range than the natural pearls. These workers found that if a suitable heavy liquid, bromoform diluted with toluene, or acetylene tetrabromide diluted with toluene, be made up to a density of 2·74, most cultured pearls will sink in the liquid, while most natural pearls will float. This provides a quick approximate test.

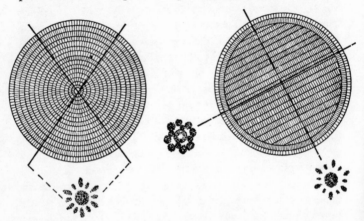

Fig. 58.—Schematic diagram of the diffraction (lauegram) method of pearl testing.

Cultured pearls show to the experienced eye blemishes like "varicose veins" which are characteristic. A string of cultured pearls "twirled" before a desk lamp will often show tell-tale gleams due to reflections from the layers of the mother-of-pearl bead, and if the light be transmitted through the bead, in certain directions where the layers are parallel to the light beam, light and dark stripes will be seen. Further, on looking down the drill canal it may be possible to see the junction layer between the bead nucleus and the outer nacreous shell.

Since the end of the Second World War there has been the cultivation of a cultured pearl without a mother-of-pearl nucleus. These pearls, which are rather characteristically bun-shaped and white in colour, are grown in a Japanese freshwater mussel called *Hyropsis schlegeli.* Clear detection of these pearls is not easy. X-ray direct pictures show certain typical marks at the centre, and the pearls glow strongly with a fluorescent light when bombarded with X-rays.

Most of the cultured pearls are grown in inland waters of Japanese bays, but there are now fisheries in the Pacific Islands and in Australia, and there are possibly a few other minor "farms."

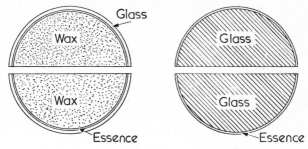

FIG. 59.—The two types of imitation pearls. Left: hollow-glass bead type. Right: solid-glass bead type.

IMITATION PEARLS

The beginning of the imitation pearl industry, which markets imitation pearl necklets from shillings to pounds, is coupled with the name of Jaquin, of Paris. There are two types of these glass bead pearls, one consists of hollow opalescent glass beads sprayed on the inside with *essence d'orient*, which is a composition made with scales from a fish, either the *bleak* or the *herring*, and parchment size. The bead is then filled with wax to make it solid. The other type consists of a solid glass (plastics or mother-of-pearl) bead upon which are placed several coats of *essence d'orient* which, after each coat has been applied, is burnished down (fig. 59). An imitation (synthetic) pearl essence is now often used for coating pearls. Some twenty coats may be applied in the better class of this type of pearl. Both these types may be detected by their smooth feel when rubbed over the teeth (a real or cultured pearl feels gritty), or by examination of the string hole which shows the glass edges and wear of the essence from the edge.

In the first type, if a spot of ink is placed on the outside, the spot will show doubling due to the reflection from the underside of the glass sphere.

Black pearls have been imitated by polished spheres of hæmatite. These are easily detected by their greatly superior density (about 5·2). Pink pearl has been imitated in pink coral, but may be detected by the surface striations of pink coral, or by the higher density of pink pearl (2·85) to coral (2·7). Any plastic imitations of pink pearl (pink pearl, which lacks iridescence, being the only one that can be imitated in the synthetic resins) may be easily identified by the extremely low density of the plastics.

CORAL, AMBER, JET

CORAL

A GEM which ranked high with the ladies of the Victorian era, coral is yet another substance which is derived from the secretion of calcium carbonate and other matter by animal life. Coral is actually the axial skeleton of the coral polyp. Many coral polypi produce "coral," but it is only in one particular member of the family that the skeleton produces the comparatively hard rose-coloured material known to jewellers as "Precious coral." This member of the coral family is known as *Corallium nobile* or *Corallium rubrum*, and, like most other corals, lives in colonies; the countless skeletons together assume a tree-like form. They are fished from the warm waters of the Mediterranean.

The composition of coral is roughly: calcium carbonate in the form of calcite (86–87 per cent); magnesium carbonate ($MgCO_3$) ($6\frac{1}{2}$–7 per cent); organic matter ($1\frac{1}{4}$–3 per cent); ferric oxide (Fe_2O_3) ($\frac{3}{4}$–2 per cent); calcium sulphate ($CaSO_4$) ($1\frac{1}{4}$–$1\frac{1}{2}$ per cent); phosphates, silica and water (small quantities). The hardness is about $3\frac{1}{2}$; the specific gravity, 2·6–2·7. The fracture is uneven or splintery and the colour varies from pure white to dark red. The various shades have different names applied to them in the trade; these may be summarized as follows:

Bianco ...	...	... pure white.
Pelle d'angelo	...	... pale flesh pink (angel's skin).
Rose pallido	...	... pale rose.
Rosa vivo	...	... bright rose.
Secondo coloro	...	... salmon colour (second colour)

Rosso	...	...	...	red.
Rosso scuro	...	...	dark red.
Arciscuro or Carbonetto	...	very dark red, often called ox-blood red.

Coral effervesces with acids, due to its carbonate of lime content, and this is a practical method of testing, as all imitations are unaffected by acid. Coral, however, might be used as a simulation for pink pearl, in which case the acid test would not apply; but careful note of the appearance and lustre, which are very different, will distinguish the one from the other. Coral is occasionally stained before being placed on the market, but the process does not seem to be permanent.

Apart from the Mediterranean source there are further fisheries around the coast of Japan. There is also a black coral, obtained from the *Antipathes spiralis*, which is fished in the Indian Ocean and around the waters of Hawaii, the latter material being used in jewellery. The density of this material, which is nearly pure conchiolin, is 1.34. A similar type of coral obtained from the Mediterranean is termed *giogetto*. Off the Cameroon coast there has been fished a blue coral which was known to the natives as *akori*. This is obtained from the *Allopara subirolcea*.

OPERCULUM

For the sake of completeness some mention may be made of another material of organic origin and consisting of carbonate of lime and conchiolin. Known as *operculum* or *shell (or Chinese) cat's-eye*, but unlike the gem cat's-eyes of chrysoberyl or quartz, etc., they do not exhibit chatoyancy and their only claim to the title "eyes" is due to their circular shape and eye-like markings of green and brown on the whitish surface.

These objects are actually secreted by a mollusc known as the *Turbo petholatus*, which in appearance, both the animal and the shell, resemble an outsize in winkles. The operculum (Latin, meaning a lid) is the process secreted by the animal to act as a door to the mouth of the shell. In the common winkle, this "door" is the well-known horny plate which is found attached to the animal, while in the Turbo the door or operculum is shelly and thick with a domed-shape outer surface. The base of these objects is flat and is covered by a brownish skin and shows spiral lines of growth.

The constitution is calcium carbonate in the form of radiating crystallites of aragonite, a small quantity of organic matter (conchiolin) and some water. The specific gravity ranges between 2·70 and 2·76; the hardness, $3\frac{1}{2}$. These shells, termed *topshells*, are found in the littorals of the tropic seas between Indo-China and the northern coast of Australia and the South Seas. These objects have little importance in jewellery.

AMBER

Compared with most of the materials used as precious and ornamental stones, amber is a youngster in geologic time, despite the fact that it is a fossil, whereas most gems had their genesis when this earth was a slowly cooling mass. Amber is the fossilized resin of certain coniferous trees which flourished in the geologic period known as Eocene, just previous to the great Ice Age, but at a time when animal life had already made its presence felt on this planet.

Transparent to opaque (bone) amber has as its most characteristic colour various tints of yellow and yellowish-red, although it may be found in shades of white, blue, red and also black, but these tints are rare. Amber is very soft, it has a hardness of only $2\frac{1}{2}$ on Mohs's scale, about the same, or slightly harder, than a finger nail. The specific gravity lies between the limits 1·00 and 1·10, that is, it is just heavier than water. The index of refraction is 1·54. It exhibits negative frictional electricity, that is it will pick up small pieces of tissue paper after being rubbed briskly on a cloth. This effect, which was one of the first phenomena to be observed with relation to magnetism and electricity, gives amber the distinction of being the parent of electricity. Amber to the Greeks was known as "electron," hence the name electricity. This frictional electricity effect must not be taken too seriously as a test for amber, as certain of the amber counterfeits may also show this. Amber, like most other gems, has several varieties, mainly characterized by the localities in which it is found, and one can do little better than to attempt to describe them in the order of their accepted importance.

BALTIC AMBER (*Succinite*). The most important of the amber-bearing localities is the Samland coast near Königsberg, East Prussia, and eastwards along the Lithuanian coastline, where the material is often washed up on the shores after storms and is also dredged from the shallow waters. This *sea amber*, as it is called, is washed out by wave action from an outcrop of amber-bearing earth beneath the Baltic Sea. Most important, however, is the method of open pit mining, where the amber is dug out of the glauconite sand known as "blue earth" (not to be confused with the "blue ground" of the Kimberley diamond pipes, which is a peridotite) by steam shovels. At the mine town of Palmnicken this *pit amber*, as it is generally termed, is washed in revolving cylinders with sand and water and graded into three groups: first those pieces which by size and clearness can be used directly as material for fashioning, this being termed *Block amber*; secondly, those pieces too small in themselves but which are clean enough to be used for *Pressed amber* (see later under "Artificial Treatment"); and thirdly, the remainder, all rough material, this being heated in retorts to obtain succinic acid, amber oil and a resin called colophony, used in making varnishes and lacquers. Amber burns with a smoky flame giving off a strong aromatic odour, hence the German name *Bernstein*; and being so light readily floats just below the surface of the sea, and so may be carried by the action of the tides and currents across the North Sea, where it is washed up on the shores of the east coast of England and on the coastline of Scandinavian countries.

BURMESE AMBER (*Burmite*) is found near the valley of the Hukong, not far from the jadeite mines in the Myitkyina district of Burma. This material may be said to be the primary source of the so-called *Chinese amber*, but much Baltic amber is now shipped to China. Burmite is generally of a pale yellow colour and is usually not so clean as the Baltic material, the mineral calcite often being an inclusion.

SICILIAN AMBER (*Simetite*) is of a darker colour, reddish hues being more common. It is found in the district around the mouth of the Simeto river, Catania. This amber is often marked by a fine bluish fluorescence not unlike that seen on oil.

ROUMANIAN AMBER (*Roumanite*), a deeper coloured amber; brownish-yellow, brown, red and black are common colours. This amber is also often found to show fluorescence. The district where the material is found is in the province of Bazau in Roumania.

Amber has also been found in Australia, the United States of America and Canada, but these finds are mainly of academic interest.

ARTIFICIAL TREATMENT. Before commenting on those materials which simulate amber some remarks must be given concerning the artificial treatment of the genuine substance. Amber can be, and often is, stained to shades deeper in colour in order to suggest aged amber (true amber darkens with age to a pleasing reddish colour); various shades of green are sometimes developed. A black is also produced. Amber is thermoplastic; that is, it softens on heating at a temperature of about 180° C. Small pieces can then be pressed together to form a mass large enough to cut; this is commercially known as *pressed amber* or *ambroid*. It may readily be detected by its fluidal structure, sharp margins of the zones of slightly different clarity and the elongated form of the included bubbles; those bubbles seen in natural amber are circular in form. Cloudy amber is often clarified by careful heating in an oil of similar refractive index, such as *rape-seed* oil. This fills the many small bubbles which are the cause of the cloudiness. Sometimes by this, or similar treatment, an attractive amber is produced which contains iridescent cracks like nasturtium leaves.

IMITATIONS

COPAL RESIN. A recent fossil resin, similar to true amber in colour and appearance, but differing in its chemical composition. Found in Zanzibar and New Zealand. The New Zealand variety is perhaps better known as *kauri gum*. Another type of this recent resin is known as *gum anime*, and has at times been found containing the remains of insects. Found in rounded lumps, copal generally has a characteristic goose skin appearance on the outside; this, of course, does not help in its distinction when the resin has been cut and fashioned for jewellery purposes. The specific gravity and the index of refraction are much about the same as for real amber; therefore the methods of detection by refractive index measurements and density determinations, and this includes the use of salt solution as a heavy liquid, are of no use to detect copal. Certain writers have made the suggestion that as amber when heated evolves hydrogen sulphide (H_2S = sulphuretted hydrogen), a piece of blotting paper moistened with a solution of lead acetate (sugar of lead) turns black in the fumes; copal does not do this. What is, perhaps, a quicker test, is to apply a drop of ether (the liquid anæsthetic, not the all-pervading medium assumed to be that which propagates the electro-magnetic waves of light) to the specimen, when, if copal, a dull spot is left, there being no dulling of the surface on natural amber; copal is softer under the knife.

GLASS is much harder and feels much colder than amber (amber being a bad conductor of heat feels warm to the touch). The density of glass is much greater than amber, generally over 2. Yellow glass can usually be detected on sight.

PLASTICS. The more important amber imitations are made of the plastic resins. A general description of these has already been given in the lesson on imitations, and hence, a comprehensive discussion will not be given now. However, as there are one or two points which it is useful to note, a short reiteration of the types is called for. The *phenol* type of *bakelite* appears to be the most common form of amber imitation, but all the bakelite types are suitable. The *celluloids* and *casein* have also been found to imitate amber; however, like bakelite, their greater density allows them to be separated from true amber by the salt solution (ten level teaspoonfuls of common salt in a tumbler of water; S.G. = $1 \cdot 12 – 1 \cdot 14$). When tested by a knife, celluloid peels, while bakelite is tough; amber chips or comes away as a powder. These plastic imitations may exhibit frictional electricity. With casein, a drop of nitric acid placed on the surface produces a blister or dull spot. The low density plastic *perspex* (S.G. = 1·18–1·19) could also simulate amber; here again the salt solution will separate. There is, however, the new plastic, *polystyrene*, which is understood to have a density of only 1·05. This might afford trouble. As it has not as yet been found as an amber substitute, and little seems to be known about its other properties, the question must be left at that. Polystyrene, however, dissolves in organic hydrocarbon liquids such as mono-bromonaphthalene, bromoform and methylene iodide.

JET

Also of vegetable origin, jet is a variety of fossil wood allied to cannel coal. It takes an excellent polish and as a gem material enjoyed a popularity in Victorian times as a medium for mourning jewellery. As in the case of coal, jet is due to the change during long years of the wood of a coniferous type of tree, the forests of which had been long buried by geologic changes. The best known and only localities of any importance are at Whitby and in the neighbouring Yorkshire dales, where it is found in the shales of the Upper Lias; and in the province of Asturia in Spain.

Jet has a low hardness, $3\frac{1}{2}$ on Mohs's scale; its density lies between the limits 1·10 and 1·40 (most generally between 1·30 and 1·35). The refractive index appears to lie between the limits 1·64 and 1·68; observed on a refractometer the shadow edge is vague and indistinct. Jet burns with a smoky flame like coal, but does not soil the fingers when handled. The material may be conveniently imitated by any of the plastics, particularly the bakelites, casein and even the hard rubber-vulcanite. The very superior and characteristic polish which is taken by jet serves to identify the genuine material from the plastics. The specific gravity of the latter may overlap the range given for jet, but in only one case, that of bakelite, does the refractive index also approximate. When a hot needle is pressed into jet the characteristic smell of burning coal is given off.

For material of a black colour in the make up of jewellery jet has, in recent years, been replaced by the harder and more durable chalcedony which has been stained black. Scotch cannel coal makes an effective substitute and, lastly, pressed amber in which a black colour has been induced gives, owing to its excellent polish, a very fine simulation of jet. The low density of amber serves for conclusive discrimination, and the black glass, sometimes called "Paris glass," is harder. Vulcanite, another substitute for jet, is identified by the rubbery smell given off when a hot needle is pressed into it.

TORTOISESHELL, IVORY

TORTOISESHELL

THIS attractive material, another substance which is rarely included in works on gem materials, consists of the epidermic plates covering the bony carapace of the *Hawksbill*, a marine turtle (*Chelone imbricata*) and does not, as its name would imply, come from the common tortoise. These plates or *blades*, as they are termed in the trade, are the actual *tortoiseshell* and names are applied to them, such as *cross-backs*, *main plates*, etc. (fig. 60). The colour varies from warm yellows mottled with rich browns to a deep reddish colour and dark brown.

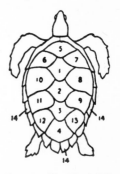

FIG. 60.—The Hawksbill turtle showing the blades of tortoiseshell. 1, 2, 3, 4, cross-backs. 5, 6, 7, 8, shoulder plates. 9, 10, 11, main plates. 12, 13, tail plates. 14, hoof.

The refractive index is round about 1·55 and the specific gravity 1·26 to 1·35. The material is thermoplastic, hence pieces may be moulded together (at the temperature of boiling water). Tortoiseshell is ably imitated by many of the plastics, notably with the so-called plastic horns—casein.

Distinction between real tortoiseshell and plastic imitations can be made by observing with a lens the internal structure. In real tortoiseshell the colour is made up of small discs of pigment, whereas the colour in the imitations is in swathes. A thin veneer of the genuine material is sometimes attached to a background of suitable plastic. This gives a baffling counterfeit. The turtle is found in

Oceania, the West Indies and the Brazilian coast and particularly the island of Celebes. Blond tortoiseshell is the clear plain yellow material obtained from the plastron or belly shield of the same turtle.

Seldom included in gemmological literature is the organic substance known as ivory, although as a material incorporated in articles of adornment it has been known from the earliest times. Ivory is supplied by the tusks of the elephant, of the rhinoceros, the tusks and cutting teeth of the hippopotamus, the tusks of the walrus, the front teeth of the narwhal, the lower teeth of the cachalot and the tusks of the mastodon and mammoth (fossil ivory).

Elephant tusks are the animal's upper incisor teeth, and in the case of the male African elephant may weigh up to 150 lbs. The females have smaller tusks which are hollow for some distance up. Indian ivory, which may excel in quality the material from Africa, is smaller in size of tusk, weighing about 50 lbs. on an average. This type is also known as the Asiatic ivory; the Indian elephant country extends from Bengal to Burma and Sumatra. Mammoth ivory is found in Siberia and the Russia of the Urals, embedded in caves and often in ice. Although harder and more brittle than the recent ivory, the fossil ivory is often spoilt by cracks. Hippopotamus ivory is hard and white, while narwhal ivory contains flaws and cracks. Walrus ivory is somewhat rare and is in many respects coarser than the material from the hippopotamus.

Ivory consists of dentine and enamel, and a percentage of organic substance which may be keratin and/or albumin. The specific gravity lies between the limits 1·70 to 1·93 and the index of refraction (vaguely identified on a refractometer) is about 1·54. The hardness appears to be about 2 to 3 on the Mohs's scale and the fracture is splintery in character. The structure is very dense and a thin section (or peeling) viewed under the microscope shows a number of wavy lines reminiscent of the hachure lines seen on old maps to represent mountains. These are called the "lines of Retzius." Ivory, when heated, produces fumes which are strongly alkaline in character (this may be ascertained by heating a small fragment in a test tube and using red litmus paper as an indicator); a drop of nitric acid tends to soften the surface of real ivory. Despite its dense character, ivory is somewhat porous and may thus be suitably stained. The pores appear to be filled with a gelatinous solution which contributes to the peculiar polish.

Ivory is simulated by all the better known plastics but the best imitation of an artificial nature is undoubtedly celluloid. The distinction is simple for celluloid peels under the knife, whereas ivory is tough, also the density of ivory is greater than celluloid. Bone which may be said to have a similarity to ivory has a greater density (1·94–2·10) and shows, when a peeling is viewed by microscope, many crack-like markings not seen in ivory. One of the most important substances which simulates ivory belongs to the vegetable kingdom and is the *corozo nut* of commerce. These nuts are obtained from the *ivory nut palm*, the *Phetelephas macrocarpa*, which grows in the hot valleys around the Andes in South America. The nuts, similar to a large Brazil nut, are the kernels of the fruit. They are very hard when ripe and have a fine grained interior, white in colour. The density of this material lies between 1·38 to 1·42; the refractive index about 1·54. When heated, in contradistinction to ivory, the material gives a strong acid reaction. A peeling of vegetable ivory viewed under a microscope, or even a strong lens will do, shows a striated pattern of oval or torpedo-shaped cells which appear to be connected together by filaments. More recently another sort of palm tree has produced a vegetable ivory, this is the *Doom palm* found growing, and also cultivated, in North and Central Africa. This "ivory," which is known botanically as from the *Hyphaene thebaica*, has the same characters as the *Corozo nut* "ivory."

UNUSUAL GEMSTONES

IN the eighth lesson a short review was given of the mineral species supplying gemstones which have an importance, and are fairly common, in the jeweller's trade. There are, however, a number of other mineral species which produce transparent crystals which, when cut into suitable forms, produce gemstones vying in beauty with many of the gems better known to jewellers. Most of these are rare, and if found cut as gems, have usually been so fashioned for the requirements of collectors of the unusual, but it is a known fact that these gems may sometimes be found mounted in jewellery, often misnamed, as in appearance they might resemble in lustre and colour some very well-known gemstone. These gems will be tabled now.

AMBLYGONITE.—A fluophosphate of aluminium and lithium $(LiAl(F,OH)PO_4)$; Triclinic; *Colours:* colourless to yellow; $H. = 6$; $S.G. = 3\cdot02$; $R.I. = 1\cdot611-1\cdot637$; *Lustre:* vitreous; localities are Brazil, U.S.A., France and Australia. A mauve-coloured amblygonite is said to be found in S.W. Africa.

ANATASE.—A native titanium oxide (TiO_2); Tetragonal; *Colour:* brown to black; $H. = 5\frac{1}{2}$ to 6; $S.G. = 3\cdot82$ to $3\cdot95$; $R.I. = 2\cdot493-2\cdot554$; *Lustre:* adamantine to metallic; localities are Switzerland and Brazil.

ANDALUSITE.—An aluminium silicate (Al_2SiO_5); Rhombic; *Colours:* green, brown and red; $H. = 7$ to $7\frac{1}{2}$; $S.G. = 3\cdot12$ to $3\cdot18$; $R.I. = 1\cdot633-1\cdot644$; *Lustre:* vitreous; *Dichroism:* strong; localities are Brazil, Burma and Ceylon. Andalusite may be mistaken for tourmaline of similar colour but may be differentiated by careful determination of the double-refraction, $0\cdot011$ for andalusite and $0\cdot020$ for tourmaline.

APATITE.—Calcium-fluorine phosphate $(Ca_4(CaF)(PO_4)_3)$; Hexagonal; *Colours:* blue-green (termed MOROXITE), yellow-green (termed ASPARAGUS STONE), pink, violet, purple and colourless; $H. = 5$; $S.G. = 3 \cdot 15$ to $3 \cdot 23$; $R.I. = 1 \cdot 63–1 \cdot 64$ to $1 \cdot 64–1 \cdot 65$; *Lustre:* vitreous to resinous; *Dichroism:* feeble; localities are Saxony, Bohemia, Maine, U.S.A., Burma and Ceylon.

AUGELITE.—A hydrated aluminium phosphate $(2Al_2O_3.P_2O_5 3H_2O)$; Monoclinic; *Colour:* colourless; $H. = 5$; $S.G. = 2 \cdot 7$; $R.I. = 1 \cdot 57–1 \cdot 58$; found in U.S.A. and Bolivia.

AXINITE.—A complex calcium-aluminium borosilicate $((Ca, Fe)_3 Al_2(B,OH)Si_4O_{15})$; Triclinic; *Colours:* brown, honey-yellow and violet; $H. = 6\frac{1}{2}$ to 7; $S.G. = 3 \cdot 27$ to $3 \cdot 29$; $R.I. = 1 \cdot 67–1 \cdot 68$; *Lustre:* vitreous; *Dichroism:* very strong; localities are France, Tasmania, Mexico and U.S.A. The name of the species is derived from the axe-like shape of the crystals.

BENITOITE.—A barium-titanium silicate $(BaTiSi_3O_9)$; Trigonal; *Colour:* sapphire blue; $H. = 6\frac{1}{2}$; $S.G. = 3 \cdot 64$ to $3 \cdot 65$; $R.I. = 1 \cdot 76– 1 \cdot 80$; *Lustre:* vitreous; *Dichroism:* strong; locality, San Benito Co., California, U.S.A. Benitoite may be differentiated from sapphire by its lower specific gravity and by its large birefringence.

BERYLLONITE. — A sodium - beryllium phosphate $(NaBePO_4)$; Rhombic; *Colours:* colourless to pale yellow; $H. = 5\frac{1}{2}$ to 6; $S.G. = 2 \cdot 80$ to $2 \cdot 85$; $R.I. = 1 \cdot 55–1 \cdot 56$; *Lustre:* vitreous; locality is at Stoneham, Maine, U.S.A.

BRAZILIANITE.—A hydrous sodium aluminium phosphate $(Al_3Na (PO_4)(OH_4))$; Monoclinic; *Colour:* yellow; $H. = 5\frac{1}{2}$; $S.G. = 2 \cdot 98– 2 \cdot 995$; $R.I. = 1 \cdot 60–1 \cdot 62$; *Lustre:* vitreous; localities, Brazil and U.S.A.

CASSITERITE.—Tin oxide (SnO_2); Tetragonal; *Colours:* red, brown, black and yellow. $H. = 6$ to 7; $S.G. = 6 \cdot 8$ to $7 \cdot 1$; $R.I. = 1 \cdot 99–2 \cdot 09$; *Lustre:* adamantine; localities, Cornwall, Bohemia, Saxony, Australia, Mexico and S. America.

DANBURITE.—A calcium borosilicate $(CaB_2Si_2O_8)$; Rhombic; *Colours:* colourless and yellow; $H. = 7$; $S.G. = 3 \cdot 00$; $R.I. = 1 \cdot 630– 1 \cdot 636$; *Lustre:* vitreous; *Dichroism:* indistinct; localities are Madagascar,

Burma, Japan and Switzerland. Danburite may resemble topaz, but its density is much lower (S.G. of topaz = 3·53 mean).

DATOLITE.—A calcium-boro-silicate $(Ca(B,OH)SiO_4)$; Monoclinic; Colour: colourless or with pale tinges of yellow or green; H. = 5; S.G. = 2·9; R.I. = 1·62–1·67; Lustre: vitreous; localities are U.S.A. and Switzerland. A massive variety brown or white in colour is found in the Canadian copper belt and on the islands of Lake Superior. This material often contains copper.

DIOPSIDE.—A calcium-magnesium silicate $(CaMg(SiO_3)_2)$; Monoclinic; Colour: green; H. = 5 to 6; S.G. = 3·20 to 3·32; R.I. = 1·67–1·70; Lustre: vitreous; Dichroism: weak; localities are Italy, U.S.A., Brazil and Ceylon. A bright green chrome diopside is found in the blue-ground at Kimberley, S. Africa, and Burma; the latter being somewhat fibrous and therefore producing cat's-eyes. Nearly-black star diopsides are found in India. Alternative names for the species are ALALITE and MALACOLITE. A massive violet-blue variety is called VIOLANE and will be further mentioned under Ornamental Stones.

DIOPTASE.—A copper silicate (H_2CuSiO_4); Trigonal; Colour: emerald-green; H. = 5; S.G. = 3·3 (3·27 to 3·35); R.I. = 1·65–1·70; Lustre: vitreous; localities are Siberia, Chili and Congo.

ENSTATITE.—A magnesium silicate $(MgSiO_3)$; Rhombic; Colour: green; H. = 5½; S.G. = 3·26 to 3·28; R.I. = 1·66–1·67; Lustre: vitreous; Dichroism: very weak; localities are South Africa and Burma.

EPIDOTE.—A calcium aluminium silicate $(Ca_2Al_2(AlOH)(SiO_4)_3)$; Monoclinic; Colours: yellow, green, brown and red; H. = 6 to 7; S.G. = 3·25 to 3·50; R.I. = 1·73–1·76; Lustre: vitreous to metallic; Dichroism: strong; localities are Italy, France, Germany and Alaska.

EUCLASE.—A beryllium silicate $(Be(AlOH)SiO_4)$; Monoclinic; Colours: colourless, pale shades of green and blue; H. = 7½; S.G. = 3·05 to 3·10; R.I. = 1·65–1·67; Lustre: vitreous; Dichroism: weak; localities are Brazil, Russia, India and Tanzania.

FIBROLITE.—An aluminium silicate (Al_2SiO_5); Rhombic; Colours: pale blue and green; H. = 7½; S.G. = 3·25; R.I. = 1·65–

1·67; *Lustre:* vitreous; *Dichroism:* strong; localities, Burma and Ceylon.

FLUORSPAR.—Calcium fluoride (CaF_2); Cubic; *Colours:* colourless, yellow, green, violet, red, pink, blue and brown. BLUE JOHN is a massive variety of fluorspar which is found in the caves and lead mines at Castleton, Derbyshire. Sometimes known as DERBYSHIRE SPAR. $H. = 4$; $S.G. = 3·18$; $R.I. = 1·43$; *Lustre:* vitreous; localities, England, France, S.W. Africa, Norway and U.S.A.

HAMBERGITE.—A beryllium borate ($Be_2(OH)BO_3$); Rhombic; *Colour:* colourless; $H. = 7\frac{1}{2}$; $S.G. = 2·25$; $R.I. = 1·55–1·62$; *Lustre:* vitreous; locality, Madagascar.

HAEMATITE.—Iron oxide (Fe_2O_3); Hexagonal; *Colour:* black; $H. = 5\frac{1}{2}$ to $6\frac{1}{2}$; $S.G. = 4·9$ to $5·3$; $R.I. = 2·94–3·22$; *Lustre:* metallic; localities, England, Germany, Spain, Scandinavia and U.S.A. Gives a red streak on unglazed china.

IDOCRASE.—A complex calcium aluminium silicate ($Ca_6Al(AlOH)(SiO_4)_5$); Tetragonal; *Colours:* yellow, green and brown; $H. = 6\frac{1}{2}$; $S.G. = 3·35$ to $3·45$; $R.I. = 1·70–1·72$; *Lustre:* vitreous; *Dichroism:* weak; localities, Italy, Siberia, Norway and U.S.A. Alternative name, VESUVIANITE. A green compact variety resembles jade and is known as CALIFORNITE, while CYPRINE is a greenish-blue variety, containing copper. A yellowish-brown variety from New York State is called XANTHITE.

IOLITE.—A hydrated magnesium (iron) aluminium silicate ($(M_9Fe)_4Al_8(OH)_2(Si_2O_7)$); Rhombic; *Colour:* violet-blue; $H. = 7$ to $7\frac{1}{2}$; $S.G. = 2·58$ to $2·66$; $R.I. = 1·53–1·54$; *Lustre:* vitreous; *Dichroism:* strong; localities are Ceylon, India, Burma and Madagascar. Alternative names for the species are CORDIERITE, DICHROITE and the incorrect term "WATER SAPPHIRE."

KORNERUPINE.—Magnesium aluminium silicate ($M_9Al_2SiO_6$); Rhombic; *Colours:* colourless, brown and yellow, blue and green; $H. = 6\frac{1}{2}$; $S.G. = 3·27$ to $3·32$; $R.I. = 1·66–1·67$; *Lustre:* vitreous; *Dichroism:* strong; localities are Madagascar, Ceylon, Saxony and Greenland.

KYANITE.—An aluminium silicate (Al_2SiO_5); Triclinic; *Colours:* green, sky-blue and colourless; $H. = 5$ to 7 (varies with direction); $S.G. = 3 \cdot 55$ to $3 \cdot 67$; $R.I. = 1 \cdot 71$–$1 \cdot 72$; *Lustre:* vitreous; *Dichroism:* marked; localities are India, Brazil, Switzerland, U.S.A. and Kenya. Sometimes spelt CYANITE.

LEUCITE.—A potassium aluminium silicate ($KAl(SiO_3)_2$); Cubic; *Colour:* colourless; $H. = 5\frac{1}{2}$ to 6; $S.G. = 2 \cdot 48$; $R.I. = 1 \cdot 51$; found in Germany, Italy and U.S.A.

MARCASITE.—Iron disulphide (FeS_2); Rhombic; *Colour:* brass yellow; $H. = 6$ to $6\frac{1}{2}$; $S.G. = 4 \cdot 8$; *Lustre:* metallic. The "marcasite" of the jewellery trade is really PYRITES, or merely cut steel or white metal.

MOLDAVITE.—A silica glass found in Bohemia and Moravia. It is amorphous and of green colour. Alternative names are WATER CHRYSOLITE or BOTTLE STONE. Moldavite is not unlike obsidian. $H. = 5\frac{1}{2}$; $S.G. = 2 \cdot 3$ to $2 \cdot 5$; $R.I. = 1 \cdot 48$ to $1 \cdot 50$.

OBSIDIAN.—A volcanic glass. Amorphous, with colours of black, red and brown, $H. = 5\frac{1}{2}$; $S.G. = 2 \cdot 3$ to $2 \cdot 5$; $R.I. = 1 \cdot 50$.

PHENAKITE.—A beryllium silicate (Be_2SiO_4); Hexagonal; *Colours:* colourless, pale yellow and pale pink; $H. = 7\frac{1}{2}$ to 8; $S.G. = 2 \cdot 95$ to $3 \cdot 00$; $R.I. = 1 \cdot 65$–$1 \cdot 66$; *Lustre:* vitreous; localities are Russia and North and South America.

POLLUCITE.—A cæsium aluminium silicate ($H_2Cs_4Al_4(SiO_3)_9$); Cubic; *Colour:* colourless; $H. = 6\frac{1}{2}$; $S.G. = 2 \cdot 86$; $R.I. = 1 \cdot 51$; *Lustre:* vitreous; localities are U.S.A. and Isle of Elba.

PYRITES.—Iron disulphide (FeS_2); Cubic; *Colour:* brass yellow; $H. = 6\frac{1}{2}$; $S.G. = 4 \cdot 84$ to $5 \cdot 10$. Pyrites is the "marcasite" of the jewellery trade.

RHODIZITE.—A borate of aluminium and potassium ($KAl_2B_3O_8$); Cubic; *Colours:* pale green and pale yellow; $H. = 8$; $S.G. = 3 \cdot 40$; $R.I. = 1 \cdot 69$; *Lustre:* vitreous to adamantine; localities are Russia and Madagascar.

RUTILE.—Titanium oxide (TiO_2); Tetragonal; *Colours:* red, brown and black; $H. = 6$ to $6\frac{1}{2}$; $S.G. = 4 \cdot 2$ to $4 \cdot 3$; $R.I. = 2 \cdot 62$–$2 \cdot 90$;

Lustre: adamantine to metallic; localities, Russia, Scandinavia, Italy, France, U.S.A., Switzerland and Madagascar. Now made synthetically.

SCAPOLITE.—An isomorphous group of minerals which are, in the main, sodium-calcium-aluminium silicates and belong to the tetragonal system; *Colours:* yellow, pink and blue; $H. = 6\frac{1}{2}$; $S.G. = 2\cdot61$ to $2\cdot70$; $R.I. = 1\cdot54-1\cdot56$ to $1\cdot55-1\cdot57$; *Lustre:* vitreous; localities, Burma, Madagascar and Brazil.

SINHALITE.—A magnesium aluminium-iron borate $(Mg(Al,Fe)BO_4)$; Rhombic; *Colour:* pale yellow-brown, greenish-to golden-brown, dark brown to black; $H. = 6\frac{1}{2}$; $S.G. = 3\cdot47$ to $3\cdot49$; $R.I. = 1\cdot67-1\cdot71$; locality, Ceylon and Burma.

STAUROLITE.—A hydrated iron-aluminium silicate $(HFeAl_5Si_2O_{13})$; Rhombic; *Colour:* reddish-brown; $H. = 7$ to $7\frac{1}{2}$; $S.G. = 3\cdot4$ to $3\cdot8$; $R.I. = 1\cdot74-1\cdot75$; localities, Switzerland and South America. Owing to their tendency to crystallize in twins having a cruciform shape the crystals have a use as amulets. Sometimes called "cross-stone."

WILLEMITE.—A zinc silicate (Zn_2SiO_4); Hexagonal; *Colours:* yellow, green, brown and reddish; $H. = 5$ to 6; $S.G. = 3\cdot89$ to $4\cdot18$; $R.I. = 1\cdot69-1\cdot71$; *Lustre:* vitreous to resinous; locality is at Franklin Furnace, New Jersey, U.S.A.

ORNAMENTAL MINERALS

THE final group of minerals to be discussed, comprise those used for purposes where, in general, a flat or a carved surface is required, such as in carved figures, the plain (or carved) sides of cigarette boxes, or for the cases of clocks.

These *ornamental stones* are often massive varieties of better-known minerals, some of which we have discussed earlier as gemstones. The ornamental stones rely, as a rule, on their characteristic colour and on their texture and banding for their beauty and attraction.

In order to complete the lesson, it will be found convenient to refer again to one or two species which have already been discussed. Such stones as Jade, Lapis Lazuli, etc., have such an importance that their double inclusion will also be of value.

BERYL.—Semi-translucent green beryl has often been fashioned in the form of carved figures, when it sometimes appears to be similar to Green Fluorspar, which is often so carved. The greater hardness of green beryl is characteristic. The constants of green beryl are the same as for the gem varieties, *i.e.* $R.I. = 1.57-1.58$, $S.G. =$ about 2.70, $H. = 7\frac{1}{2}$ to 8.

MALACHITE.—A hydrated copper carbonate $(Cu_2(OH)_2CO_3)$; Monoclinic; *Colour:* green with a silky texture; $R.I. = 1.65-1.90$; $S.G. = 3.74$ to 3.95; $H. = 4$; *Lustre:* vitreous to adamantine; localities Russia, Chile, Belgian Congo, S. Africa, Australia and the U.S.A. Malachite, like all carbonates, effervesces when acted on by an acid and is mainly fashioned as polished plates, or occasionally in cabochon forms.

AZURITE.—A hydrated copper carbonate, with a slightly different formula to Malachite ($Cu_3(OH)_2(CO_3)_2$); Monoclinic; *Colour:* dark blue; *R.I.* = 1·73–1·83; *S.G.* = 3·77 to 3·89; *H.* = $3\frac{1}{2}$ to 4; *Lustre:* vitreous; localities, Russia, Chile, S.W. Africa, U.S.A. and France. Sometimes known as CHESSYLITE, azurite, like malachite, is affected with acids.

AZUR-MALACHITE is malachite veined with azurite.

VIOLANE.—Near diopside ($CaMg(SiO_3)_2$); *Colour:* violet-blue; *R.I.* = about 1·69; *S.G.* = 3·23; *H.* = 6; *Lustre:* waxy.

RHODOCHROSITE.—Manganese carbonate ($MnCO_3$); Trigonal; *Colour:* rose-red or yellow or brown; *R.I.* = 1·60–1·82; *S.G.* = about 3·70; *H.* = 4; *Lustre:* vitreous or pearly; localities, South and North America, Hungary and Saxony. Being a carbonate, rhodochrosite effervesces with an acid. Sometimes known as INCA-ROSE or ROSINCA, from a fanciful idea of its use by the Inca peoples.

RHODONITE.—A manganese silicate ($MnSiO_3$); Triclinic; *Colour:* rose-pink; *R.I.* = 1·73–1·74; *S.G.* = 3·5 to 3·7; *H.* = 5 to 6; *Lustre:* vitreous; localities, Russia and U.S.A. Unlike Rhodochrosite, this material does *not* effervesce with acid.

THULITE.—A calcium aluminium silicate ($Ca_2Al_2(AlOH)(SiO_4)_3$); Rhombic; *Colour:* rose-pink; *R.I.* = about 1·70; *S.G.* = 3·12; *H.* = about $6\frac{1}{2}$; *Lustre:* vitreous; found at Telemark in Norway.

APOPHYLLITE.—A hydrated potassium calcium silicate ($HK)_2Ca(SiO_3)_2H_2O$; Tetragonal; *Colours:* white ringed with shades of yellow, green and red; *R.I.* = about 1·53; *S.G.* = 2·3 to 2·4; *H.* = $4\frac{1}{2}$ to 5; *Lustre:* vitreous to pearly; localities, Germany, India, Sweden.

FLUORSPAR.—The calcium fluoride has been treated under the unusual gemstones, as the clear material has been fashioned into cut stones. The inclusion here is made on the knowledge that the material has been used for the carving of small figures, despite the easy cleavage of fluorspar. The greenish material resembles, to some extent, the greenish beryl, the latter mineral is much harder, has a higher index of refraction and a lower density, and is doubly refractive.

	H.	R.I.	S.G.
FLUOR	4	1·43	3·18
BERYL	7½-8	1·57-1·58	2·70

LAPIS LAZULI has been treated under the lesson on species. It is included here as the material is often used for small *objets d'art*.

DUMORTIERITE.—A complex aluminium-borosilicate $(Al(AlO)_7 (BOH)(SiO_4)_3$; Rhombic; *Colour:* blue and violet; $R.I. = 1·67-1·68$; $S.G. = 3·26$ to $3·36$; $H. = 7$; strongly dichroic; localities, U.S.A., Norway, Madagascar, France and S.W. Africa.

CHRYSOCOLLA.—A hydrated copper silicate of variable formula; Probably amorphous; *Colour:* green and greenish-blue; $R.I. =$ about $1·50$; $S.G. = 2·0$ to $2·2$; $H. = 2$ to 4; *Lustre:* vitreous to earthy; localities, Russia, Chile and U.S.A. A rock-like mixture, mainly chrysocolla, which comes from Israel is used for ornamental purposes.

VARISCITE.—A hydrous aluminium-phosphate $(AlPO_4 2H_2O)$; Rhombic; *Colour:* green; $R.I. =$ about $1·58$; $S.G. =$ about $2·5$; $H. = 4$ to 5; *Lustre:* vitreous; locality, U.S.A. Alternative name UTALITE.

WARDITE.—A hydrous aluminium phosphate $(Al_2(OH)_3 PO_4 + \frac{1}{2}H_2O)$; Probably amorphous; *Colour:* light-green to bluish-green; $S.G. = 2·77$; $H. = 5$; *Lustre:* vitreous; locality, U.S.A.

ODONTOLITE.—A fossil bone or ivory-stained blue by vivianite, an iron-phosphate; *Colour:* blue; $S.G. = 3·00$ to $3·25$; localities, France and Russia. "Fizzes" with acid.

TURQUOISE has been dealt with in the lesson on the gem species. Its inclusion here is due to the use of this material in mosaics, etc. (especially by the Ancient Incas of S. America), and, as several of the materials mentioned under "ornamental stones," simulate turquoise; such materials are: ODONTOLITE, WARDITE, VARISCITE.

HOWLITE.—A silico-borate of calcium $(8CaO.5B_2O_3.6SiO_2.6H_2O)$; Monoclinic (?); *Colour:* white, sometimes with black veining; $H. = 3\frac{1}{2}$; $S.G. = 2·58$; mean $R.I. = 1·59$. The material is stained blue and may then imitate turquoise. Howlite is found in California.

CHALCEDONY, another material which has already been dealt with under QUARTZ, ONYX, AGATES, etc., has a use as an ornamental stone. Notice must also be taken of the stained chalcedony.

SMITHSONITE.—A zinc carbonate ($ZnCO_3$); Trigonal; *Colour:* green and greenish-blue, also more commonly white or greyish and yellow; *R.I.* = 1·62–1·85; *S.G.* = 4·3 to 4·65; *H.* = 5; *Lustre:* vitreous to pearly; localities, Greece, Sardinia and New Mexico. The bluish-green variety is sometimes known under the name BONAMITE.

LAZULITE.—An iron (magnesium) aluminium-phosphate ($H_2Fe Al_2P_2O_{10}$); Monoclinic; *Colour:* blue; *R.I.* = 1·61–1·64; *S.G.* = about 3·1; *H.* = 6; *Lustre:* vitreous; markedly dichroic; localities, Sweden, Austria, U.S.A. and Brazil.

SERPENTINE.—An alteration product from the decomposition of olivine and other silicates; *Colour:* green (most commonly); *R.I.* = 1·49 to 1·57; *S.G.* = 2·5 to 2·6; *Lustre:* resinous or greasy; *H.* = $2\frac{1}{2}$ to 4. One variety, known as BOWENITE, simulates jade and is remarkable as having a higher *S.G.* (2·6–2·8) and is much harder, viz. 5 to 6. "KOREA JADE" is a fancy name for serpentine.

The JADES have been previously discussed and only require inclusion here, as several of the minerals mentioned in this lesson simulate them (see p. 199).

CALCITE (MARBLE).—A massive calcium-carbonate ($CaCO_3$); Trigonal; *Colour:* white and other colours, veined in many shades; *R.I.* = 1·48–1·65; *S.G.* = 2·71; *H.* = 3.

EGYPTIAN MARBLE is black, with yellow veining.

SHELL MARBLE consists of fossil shells.

LUMACHELLA (Fire Marble) is a shell-marble, from which a fire-like chatoyancy is emitted when the polished plate is turned in different directions.

PARIAN MARBLE is white.

RUIN MARBLE is yellow, with sections of a brown colour, due to the infiltration of iron oxide.

ONYX MARBLE is banded marble.

"BRAZILIAN ONYX," or "MEXICAN ONYX," is onyx marble of greenish colour.

Marble, like all calcites, effervesces with an acid.

STEATITE.—A massive variety of talc, a hydrated magnesium silicate $(Mg_3(OH)_2Si_4O_{10})$; *Colour:* white or grey, tinged with green or red; *R.I.* = 1·54–1·59; *S.G.* = about 2·75; *H.* = 1, may be harder, due to impurities. Steatite, owing to its soapy feel, is often termed SOAPSTONE. The material is often used for carving small figures.

AGALMATOLITE may be soapstone (steatite) or a massive variety of the mineral PINITE; *Colour:* green, brown or yellow; *S.G.* = 2·78 to 2·81; *H.* = $2\frac{1}{2}$ to $3\frac{1}{2}$. This material is also used for small carvings.

MEERSCHAUM.—A hydrated magnesium silicate $(H_4Mg_2Si_3O_{10})$; *Colour:* white; *R.I.* = about 1·52; *S.G.* = about 2; *H.* = 2 to $2\frac{1}{2}$; locality, Asia Minor. Mineralogical name is SEPIOLITE. The material is used for the bowls of smoking pipes.

GYPSUM (ALABASTER).—A hydrated calcium-sulphate $(CaSO_4$ $2H_2O)$; Monoclinic; *Colour:* white; *R.I.* = about 1·52; *S.G.* = 2·32 (pure) (2·2–2·4); *H.* = 2; *Lustre:* pearly to sub-vitreous; localities, England, U.S.A. and Italy.

SATIN SPAR may be either a fibrous variety of Gypsum, or a similarly fibrous Calcite (marble).

PSEUDOPHITE.—A hydrated silicate of aluminium magnesium; Monoclinic; *Colour:* grey-green to black; *R.I.* = 1·57; *S.G.* = 2·60 to 2·85; *H.* = $2\frac{1}{2}$; localities, Styria, Switzerland, Italy, Austria, Norway and Sweden. Known commercially as "Styrian Jade."

PREHNITE.—A hydrated calcium aluminium silicate; Rhombic; *Colour:* light green, oil-green and yellow; *R.I.* = 1·62–1·65; *S.G.* = 2·80 to 2·95; *H.* = 6–$6\frac{1}{2}$; localities, North America, France and Australia.

GROSSULAR GARNET (massive variety):—A calcium-aluminium silicate; Cubic; *Colour:* green, yellow, pink, red, brown, etc.; *R.I.* = 1·72–1·74; *S.G.* = 3·40 to 3·50; locality, South Africa. Known also as "Transvaal or South African Jade."

	S.G.	R.I. (mean).	Hardness.
Nephrite ... ... (Jade, part.)	2·95 to 3·1	1·62	6½
Jadeite ... ... (Jade, part.)	3·30 to 3·50	1·66	6½ to 7
Pseudophite... ... ... ("Styrian Jade")	2·60 to 2·85	1·57	2½
Prehnite	2·80 to 2·95	1·63	6 to 6½
Massive Grossular Garnet ... ("South African or Transvaal Jade.")	3·40 to 3·50	1·73	6½ to 7
Serpentine ... ... ("Bowenite," "Verd-antique," "New Jade," "Williamsite" and "Korea Jade")	2·50 to 2·65	1·50 to 1·57	2½ to 4 ("Bowenite" 5½ to 6)
Aventurine Quartz... ... ("Indian Jade.")	2·65 to 2·66	1·55	7
Chalcedony (Chrysoprase). ("Swiss Jade.")	2·60 to 2·65	1·55	7
Microcline Feldspar ... ("Amazon Jade.")	2·54 to 2·57	1·53	6 to 6½
Idocrase ... ... ("Californite.")	3·35 to 3·45	1·72	6½
Smithsonite ... ... ("Bonamite.")	4·30 to 4·65	1·62 to 1·85	5
Agalmatolite ... ... ("Figure-stone.")	2·785 to 2·815		2½
Saussurite	3·2	1·70	6½ to 7

MICROCLINE (FELDSPAR).—A potassium-aluminium silicate; Triclinic; *Colour:* green, brown, etc.; $R.I. = 1·52–1·53$; $S.G. = 2·54$ to $2·57$; $H. = 6$ to $6\frac{1}{2}$; locality, U.S.A. and Russia. Sometimes termed "Amazon Jade."

SAUSSURITE.—A decomposed feldspar, white to greenish-grey, and allied to Zoisite. $S.G. = 2·75$ to $3·2$; $H. = 6\frac{1}{2}$ to 7.

CALIFORNITE.—A massive variety of IDOCRASE, which see.

QUARTZ.—Rock crystal and Rose quartz is used for carvings, while aventurine quartz containing flakes of chromium mica is termed "INDIAN JADE." Constants as for crystalline quartz.

BLUE JOHN is a massive variety of the mineral FLUORSPAR, which is used for small ornamental objects.

LABRADORITE (FELDSPAR).—A variety of plagioclase, showing a play of colour due to lamellar twinning.

SODALITE.—A sodium aluminium silicate which forms dodecahedral crystals of the cubic system. It has an importance in gemmology only in its massive form when it is used as an ornamental stone or as "tumbled" pieces. The stone is blue in colour and resembles to some extent the lapis lazuli. Sodalite has a hardness of $5\frac{1}{2}$ to 6; a density of $2·15$ to $2·35$ and a refractive index of $1·48$. The material comes from Ontario, Canada; Norway; and the U.S.A. A beautiful semi-translucent sodalite comes from south of the Kunene river which divides South-west Africa from Angola.

INDEX

Note: Pages in heavy type indicate a principal description.